"I . . . I HAD TO SEE YOU," MELISSA STAMMERED, HER LOWER LIP TREMBLING.

"What for?" Brandon retorted caustically.

"Because I love you," she whispered. "Because I'm miserable without you. Because. . . ." She faltered, knowing her words were wasted against his flint-hard resistance. "Because Jana needs you. She thinks of you almost as a father," she finished lamely, hoping the mention of her daughter would make Brandon forget the pain she had caused him.

His face flushed with anger. "Jana?" he questioned disbelievingly. "She has me any time she needs me, and she knows that. You could take a lesson from that little lady, Melissa. She accepts people as they are, which is more than I can say for her mother."

CANDLELIGHT ECSTASY SUPREMES

BRIGHT FLAME, DISTANT STAR

Blair Cameron

A CANDLELIGHT ECSTASY SUPREME

Published by
Dell Publishing Co., Inc.
1 Dag Hammarskjold Plaza
New York, New York 10017

ISBN: 0-440-10832-2

Printed in the United States of America

First printing—June 1985

Dedicated with love to our fathers: Walter J. Scharmack, H. M. Blair, and O. Earl Neumeier.

To Our Readers:

Candlelight Ecstasy is delighted to announce the start of a brand-new series—Ecstasy Supremes! Now you can enjoy a romance series unlike all the others—longer and more exciting, filled with more passion, adventure, and intrigue—the stories you've been waiting for.

In months to come we look forward to presenting books by many of your favorite authors and the very finest work from new authors of romantic fiction as well. As always, we are striving to present the unique, absorbing love stories that you enjoy most—the very best love has to offer.

Breathtaking and unforgettable, Ecstasy Supremes will follow in the great romantic tradition you've come to expect *only* from Candlelight Ecstasy.

Your suggestions and comments are always welcome. Please let us hear from you.

Sincerely,

The Editors
Candlelight Romances
1 Dag Hammarskjold Plaza
New York, New York 10017

CHAPTER ONE

"Damn this rush hour traffic!" Melissa Collins Bennett exploded uncharacteristically, flicking up the car's defrosting switch to high in an effort to clear the condensation forming on the windows. "And this cold rain is only making matters worse."

"Calm down, Melissa," her roommate, Julia Raymond, soothed as she braked, slowing to a snail's pace in a long line of red taillights. "What's the matter with you? You're not usually so jumpy."

"Well, don't you think that five thirty in the evening is a preposterous hour to schedule a law seminar?" Melissa asked irritably.

"That's Brandon for you," Julia chuckled. "Always unpredictable. And really, to be fair, he's a fiend for time management. He uses every minute of his day, and he expects those around him to do the same. Since he was forced to cancel speaking at our graduation exercises because of a conflicting trial date, I think it was generous of him to offer to give us this time, even if it was on terribly short notice."

"I've never heard that generosity was one of his strong points," Melissa commented wryly.

"I couldn't entirely agree with that. I've seen times when he was quite generous," Julia countered. "It's likely he had to fly to Seattle anyway, for some reason or other, but nevertheless, he is giving us his time, and time means everything to him."

"He's a friend of Professor Burke's, isn't he?" Melissa asked, stubbornly refusing to admit the validity of Julia's argument.

"Yes. They went to Harvard graduate school together."

"I don't see how they could be very close friends," Melissa snapped.

"What do you mean? I think they are."

"Well, this afternoon I just about decided to boycott—no, I mean *woman*cott—this whole thing," Melissa muttered glumly as four lanes of traffic came to a full stop.

"Why?" Julia looked at her friend in amazement. "It's a real honor to be chosen to attend. Brandon specifically requested that he address only the top twenty-five in the class, and . . ."

"That in itself is the act of an arrogant man, as far as I'm concerned," Melissa interrupted, sapphire eyes glinting dangerously in the glow of the oncoming headlights.

"Why are you angry with a man you've never even met? I know you've followed his career with interest. Why this sudden change in attitude? When I saw the list, I noticed that you and I were the only women who made it."

"I know that," Melissa retorted. "And I was pleased, very pleased—until this afternoon in class when Professor Burke was forced to defend his selections to some disgruntled students. During his explanation the professor casually let out that Brandon Kade doesn't think women are particularly well suited to be trial lawyers, because he thinks they're unable to reason as logically as men and can't keep their emotions under control as well as men. When Brenda Taylor heard that, she slapped her books down on the desk and walked out. As the door slammed behind her, I noticed a couple of the guys smirking. Professor Burke is such a fair-minded man, he was upset by the episode too.

"Frankly"—Melissa shifted in the bucket seat—"instead of feeling smug that I'm included tonight, I feel more like a traitor."

"I know how you feel," Julia commiserated, with a nod of her sleekly coiffed head. "But staying away from this seminar is not the way to combat that sort of thing. The only way to change anything in this world is for us to become even more visible and involved." Their lane of traffic slowly started moving again as a distant siren wailed bleakly through the darkening streets.

"Well," Melissa said, "I have a suspicion the only reason we were included is because Brandon Kade's such a close friend of your family." Having no desire to hurt Julia, she regretted this petulant remark almost before it left her mouth. Mentally she resolved to simmer down and keep *her* emotions under control no matter what the egotistical attorney might say to provoke a reaction during the seminar.

"Our class standing was the only criterion Professor Burke used," Julia reminded her somewhat coldly.

Damn, Melissa thought remorsefully, I did hurt her with that thoughtless remark. She knew how hard Julia had worked to make it on her own. Coming to Seattle to attend law school, rather than staying in California, had been part of Julia's attempt to escape the aura of her prestigious father's influence. But even here, in the eyes of some professors, Julia was still the federal judge's daughter.

"I'm sorry," Melissa said. "I guess I'm nervous. Meeting 'the great Brandon Kade' would make any aspiring lawyer a little jittery, don't you think?"

"I wouldn't know," Julia answered. "He's almost like a brother to me. But there's one good thing about all this."

"What's that?" Melissa asked.

"It's gotten you out of your customary jeans and blazer and into that blouse I gave you for your birthday, which I might add, you've never worn before."

Reddening, Melissa put her hand up to touch the ruffled neck of the ice-blue confection.

"It's nice to see your legs in something other than striped knee socks and clogs too. I'd almost forgotten you owned that navy suit, and the last time I saw those pumps they were in your closet being worn by a tennis racket."

"I only wore this so I wouldn't look like your country cousin," Melissa shot back pertly.

"Oh, really? It's never bothered you before. Are you sure meeting Brandon Kade didn't have something to do with your choice of clothing? He's a dynamite hunk, or so most women seem to think."

"Don't be ridiculous," Melissa said uneasily. "What do I care what Brandon Kade thinks? Why would he even notice me?" But to herself she had to admit that any woman under the age of eighty meeting the dashing young criminal attorney, considered by some to be the best defense lawyer in the country, would be concerned about her appearance.

"Because you're a beautiful woman, when you choose to be," Julia answered, inching the car over toward the next exit, "and you'll be the only woman there besides me. He'll notice you all right. But I shouldn't tease you." Her large, slightly almond-shaped eyes softened, her tone gentled. "It's great to see you dressed up. You've been 'one of the fellows' far too long.

"For three years I've watched you deliberately shy away from anyone who showed the slightest romantic interest in you. Sonny's been dead a long time. Don't you think it's time for you to start living again? Isn't that what commencement means?"

Biting her lower lip, Melissa looked away. During the countless long talks she and Julia had shared in their Queen Anne Hill apartment, she'd come to grips with her husband's senseless death and had justified, in her own mind, the necessity for the repeated weeks of separation from her young daughter that her need to prepare for a career had imposed. Julia had also helped her accept the fact that Laurence Bennett, Sr., her father-in-law, had been right in insisting that her daughter, Jana, remain in a stable home environment with him in Alaska while she sought her degree.

Six semesters of law school would have been impossible for Melissa to have completed without Julia's support—she knew that. She'd caught the flight to Anchorage whenever the school's calendar had afforded even a three-day break, unable to pass up any chance to be home with Jana. Frequently she'd flown through the night, arriving back on the campus directly from the airport, only to face her first class bleary-eyed and exhausted. Countless times, Julia had helped make it possible for her to go—by delivering a paper to the typist, lending Melissa her notes whenever bad weather had delayed Melissa's return, or by doing other small but important acts of kindness that had given Melissa the extra time the commuting back and forth had taken. Melissa knew she would have broken down without the frequent contact with her daughter that these trips had provided.

There was no doubt about it, she was going to miss her best friend and roommate when they graduated from law school the following week and each went her separate way: Julia to be married to Scott Lowell, a promising young associate in Brandon Kade's law firm, and she to return home to her daughter, Jana, now five years old.

Julia was right, Melissa admitted silently. Her comment about being one of the fellows had been only too accurate. Going to law school had helped her avoid facing up to the future as a woman. But school was almost over, and at twenty-eight she was going to have to face the world again. She had to make a new life for herself and for her fatherless daughter.

Reluctantly, Melissa nodded her golden head. "You're right. It does mean a new beginning. I've been doing a lot of thinking about just that lately. I'm going to be lost without you, Julia."

"I feel the same way." Julia smiled warmly. "Melissa, why don't you and Jana come home with me after graduation next week? I've been very upset thinking we wouldn't live together like this ever again. We've had such fun. I wouldn't have missed having this time with you for anything."

"Me either," Melissa admitted.

Julia continued persuasively, "You and Jana could have a whole suite to yourselves, and you could vacation with her in the sun for as long as you like. I'd love having you both there, and I know my parents would be delighted."

Melissa considered. She wasn't surprised at Julia's suggestion, since her friend had invited her to come to La Jolla every vacation since they'd been at school. She'd never gone, knowing her father-in-law expected her to come home. She mentally contrasted the cool, brief summer of the Alaskan mainland with the hot sun-filled days of the southern California coast. Certainly, just this once, she could do as she wanted. How pleasant it would be to sleep late, to swim and play with Jana—to enjoy life while spending a few final weeks with Julia. Since she would be going home to Alaska to stay after that, she doubted her father-in-law would object too strenuously, if at all, to the plan.

She still had one concern. "You know, I'm not getting married, so I can't afford to wait until February to take the bar exams like you intend to do. I'll have to cram from now until the end of July to get ready to pass the Alaska bar. That might be a problem for you, because I won't always be free to take care of Jana," she warned.

"That's no problem at all. We've got so many people around who'd love to have the chance to play with a child again. I'm not sure Mother and Dad have ever forgiven me for growing up." Julia smiled. "Seriously, she'll never be at a loss for something to do, or someone to care for her."

"If you're sure . . . ?"

"I'm sure!" Julia reaffirmed.

"I suppose I could fly home for a couple of days to take the bar that last week in July, then I'd still have two weeks before the wedding to be free . . ."

"Free . . . free!!" they chorused.

"Of course we'll come," Melissa stated emphatically.

Julia did a double take. "Did I hear right?"

Melissa nodded, a grin lighting her face.

"At long last! I want that in writing, Counselor, but remember until we can get to a notary, a verbal agreement is as binding as a written one," Julia joked as she turned into the main entrance of the campus.

Despite the heavy traffic they arrived at the student lot a full ten minutes before five thirty, only to drive in circles looking for parking. Having almost despaired of ever finding an empty space, Melissa noticed a rain-soaked student running through one of the lots and suggested to Julia that they follow him to his car. They waited impatiently as he routinely started his car and casually pulled from the spot, before Julia could whip her sports coupe into the space he vacated.

The two young women made an unusual contrast of feminine beauty as they ran from the car to the lecture building under the cover of a single cream-colored umbrella. Melissa was a "summer": her clear, fair, peaches-and-cream skin glowed under a cap of radiant blond hair; her wide-set deeply blue eyes, rimmed with sable golden-tipped lashes, sparkled like sapphires in her oval face with its charmingly pointed chin. Petitely lovely in her short ink-navy wool jacket with its softly gathered skirt, she bore a startling resemblance to Diana, Princess of Wales. Julia, her raven hair falling in a neat curve, was an olive-toned "winter": tall, willowy, with smoke gray eyes set above high cheekbones, she was strikingly attired in a modish burgundy jacket dress. At twenty-five, Julia was elegantly sophisticated.

On the columned portico as Melissa quickly shook the rain from the umbrella, the two sighed and exchanged glances, sharing the unspoken realization that they would soon no longer be students at the stately old ivy-covered university that held so many common memories for them.

With a staccato clicking of heels they hurried down the marble corridor of Rainier Hall and seated themselves in a small amphitheater with twenty-three other students expectantly awaiting the arrival of the prominent attorney.

Melissa had known for months that she would meet Brandon Kade when he served as best man at Julia and Scott's wedding, but she'd expected the meeting to come in late summer and felt strangely nervous that it was being thrust upon her now. She hoped she hadn't given Julia an inkling of the anxiety she felt about meeting him. Was it his celebrity status that was so disturbing to her? she wondered. Although her father-in-law was a powerful, highly respected entrepreneur in Anchorage, his social circle in the new American frontier of Alaska was democratically made up of self-made men, like himself, and their families. She'd always been comfortable among those people even though most of them possessed great wealth and local prestige, but in her mind Brandon Kade seemed in another category altogether.

She knew Julia felt completely differently, having known the handsome cleft-chinned lawyer since she was a little girl. Her father had guided Kade through his career, and Melissa knew the two men had remained close personal friends. Actually, it was surprising that Melissa hadn't met Kade before this, but his brief trips to Seattle had usually coincided with her own frequent flights back home.

Julia's whisper interrupted her reverie, as male voices could be heard in the hall. "I'll try to score a point for Brenda," Julia promised. "Brandon's a past master of evasiveness when he chooses to be, but I intend to pin him down if I possibly can. Hang on to your seat. He may be a lot of things, but he's never dull."

Though Melissa had seen Brandon Kade several times on TV, she was unprepared for the dynamic force of his presence when he entered the room beside Professor Burke only seconds later. Eric Burke was a tall man, but black-haired Brandon Kade was considerably taller and larger.

"Ladies and gentlemen," Professor Burke began. "It is my pleasure to introduce to you this afternoon a distinguished colleague whom I am privileged to call my friend. . . ."

During Professor Burke's lengthy introduction, Brandon Kade surveyed the students seated in semicircular, progressively elevated rows. It seemed to Melissa that he looked at each one of them with his piercing gray-blue eyes as though sizing them up as prospective jurors. His alluring smile hinted at sardonic condescension, tempered with kindliness. She could see how a jury would be at once intimidated and captivated by his charismatic charm.

When she received his scrutinizing appraisal, it seemed he took a long time before moving on to the next person. Feeling her body go hot, she knew that a deep, uncontrollable blush was spreading from her throat to her forehead. He seemed arrogant and disdainful, but instead of being annoyed, she was flattered he had given her so much attention. She was increasingly fascinated by this magnetic man whose wealth, activities, and talents were celebrated by the entire nation.

The prospective lawyers were conditioned by Brandon Kade's reputation to accept him as a proven courtroom deity. As he began lecturing, Melissa felt herself stirred by the resonant voice that filled the hushed chamber.

"I'll begin by reviewing the origins of law, the basis of all you've learned these past three years. It may seem elementary, but its message is as fresh and applicable today as it was in the first century of the Christian era, when Tacitus wrote that primitive man had no evil desires. Blameless and innocent, early man lived a simple life free of compulsions or penalties. Likewise where no recognized wrongs existed, fear imposed no prohibitions. Criminality was born with the idea of privately held property. Ownership became synonymous with right. The more property one controlled the more influential one became. Influence led to prestige, and the prestigious created laws to protect property and persons of property. Justice was created to serve the few with material means. . . ."

Melissa half listened to his words, trying to discern what made Brandon Kade so different from all the other men in the room. He was impeccably dressed in a dark blue, beautifully tailored three-piece suit, white silk shirt, and classically somber tie, and even the unflattering fluorescence of the amphitheater lighting failed to detract from his appeal. What looked like an expensive ring and watch glinted with a silvery sheen as he gestured.

In constant fluid motion, he spoke directly to each person in turn, so that each felt he was addressing only her or him. It seemed to Melissa that he singled her out in this manner more than the others, but she thought that perhaps everyone felt the same way. There was no doubt about it: Brandon Kade came across as brilliant, sincere, trustworthy, and important; completely in control of his subject matter and his listeners. Observing him, Melissa was sure his persuasive powers were such that he could convince anyone it was midnight in the glaring light of noon. Gradually she became aware that his speech was drawing to a close.

"The incidence of unprecedented cases I've cited this afternoon all lead inescapably to a simple truth. As Tacitus concluded, all subsequent laws, other than those directed against specific societal offenses, have been forcible creations of class warfare designed to fulfill the deplorable purpose of granting unconstitutional powers to the few. The problem of inequitable legislation is as vital today as it was then. We can't afford to take a narrow, case-by-case view of the law. We must work vigilantly to insure that any new legislation is equitable legislation—equitable for all!

"The message I want to impress upon you this afternoon, as the top scholars in your class, is that you owe it to the ethos of your creed to spend a substantial portion of your career defending those people who find themselves victims of the system, thereby obtaining just rulings that will have far-reaching implications for others. That is our mission as responsible lawyers. I welcome you to our ranks."

By the time the energetic applause had subsided, he was behind the podium, his engaging smile showing perfect white teeth against a deep attractive tan. "I will now answer your questions, if I am able," he announced.

Melissa sat silently as hands were raised and questions directed to Brandon Kade. She saw with growing respect how skillfully he evaded being drawn into any type of argument or political discussion. When Julia raised her hand, she was immediately recognized.

"Tell me, please, Mr. Kade," Julia asked, her eyes wide with feigned innocence, "just why you feel women are ill equipped for the law profession."

"I've never said women are ill equipped," he drawled smoothly with just a hint of a melodious southern accent, admiring Julia's shapely form as she stood. Melissa suddenly felt the full sweep of his eyes, which did not stop until they had included her own slender body from the tip of her toes to her sparkling eyes. "What I have said is that there are many places for women in the law profession, but I'm not sure they're most effective arguing before the bench."

Julia persisted sweetly. "Could you cite your reasons for that erroneous conclusion, Mr. Kade?"

Melissa admired her friend's cool demeanor and superb self-control. She feared her own reaction in similar circumstances might not have been so restrained.

"Are you sure you want me to answer that, Miss Raymond?" he bantered, leaning back, resting both elbows on the podium behind him.

Julia calmly ignored his question. "I believe you just finished making a speech about your concern that inequalities of rank and prejudice cause inequitable legislation. Don't you feel perhaps *your* prejudices are causing some inequitable practices?"

"Good point!" Melissa whispered softly. She noticed that

the entire room was silent, attentively awaiting the response of the "great man" to this blunt, hard-hitting attack.

Brandon Kade didn't move a muscle. A tolerant smile upon his lips, he continued to lounge against the podium. But Melissa sensed his posture to be deceptive.

After a long, increasingly uncomfortable pause, which Melissa knew was a practiced courtroom tactic deliberately aimed at disarming an opponent, he spoke. "I'm flattered that you think my personal opinions could have any far-reaching effects, but the women presently practicing in courtrooms and sitting on benches as high as the Supreme Court might disagree with you."

"Is one token woman out of nine your idea of equality?"

"I'm afraid I'm not a social statistician, only a humble defense attorney," he said with a devilish smile. Summarily dismissing her, he straightened to his full height and went on to other questions.

Melissa bit her lip. How could he get the upper hand so easily? After all, Julia was merely paraphrasing and giving back to him what he'd said he believed himself. It seemed he upheld a convenient double standard: one set of rules and obligations for the rest of the world, and quite another for the "humble" Mr. Brandon Kade.

When Julia calmly sat down, Melissa looked sideways at her friend, expecting to see some sign that she was upset. To her surprise she saw that Julia was smiling, apparently unperturbed by the interchange.

During the remainder of the seminar Melissa was disturbed. She felt guilty for not having publicly allied herself with Julia. Not only out of loyalty to her friend but also because of her own personal convictions, she considered interrupting the proceedings to bring back the question Brandon Kade had refused to answer satisfactorily. But she was not comfortable with this. Puzzled by Julia's capitulation, she was uncertain whether Julia wanted to pursue the subject further.

But more than that, Melissa grudgingly recognized, her silence stemmed from her reluctance to deliberately call Brandon Kade's attention to herself. She felt that the handsome attorney's gaze rested on her far too frequently as it was. Foolishly affected by the almost flirtatious looks he turned toward her, she sternly upbraided herself for being even slightly interested in a man with such a condescending attitude toward women—especially one who had a Casanova reputation.

Still the portions she'd listened to of the man's speech had been surprising. He'd appeared sincere, yet many of the views he'd expressed had seemed at odds with his public image. Just how much of his own time did he devote to altruistic ends? Was this another case of "Do as I say, not as I do"? Or, as Julia had implied, was there a hidden side of generosity to this imposing man?

Brandon Kade courteously climbed toward them as Melissa and Julia began to descend the broad concrete steps of the amphitheater.

"Forgive me, Julia, for not answering your question from the floor." Melissa watched as his firm lips curved in an irresistibly imploring smile. Was she seeing a glimmer of the private man, instead of the public image?

He continued, "I know that my belief concerning the inability of women to be first-rate trial lawyers has been a long-standing point of friction between us. I didn't want any personal displays of antagonism to disrupt the seminar. I suspected you wanted to take the bench, place me on trial, and convict me then and there in front of a jury of your peers." Melissa detected a teasing note in his deep voice.

"You deserve to be tarred and feathered. That'd be just right for someone with your archaic ideas," Julia retorted mischievously.

"And run out of town on a rail, I suppose?"

"You got it."

"Is that a very ladylike verdict to be handed down by a woman judge?" he bantered, his eyes sparkling with humor.

While addressing Julia, he turned his gaze to Melissa for an instant, taking in her full breasts, slender waist, and curvaceous hips. She felt a peculiar weakening of her knees. Must be the damned high-heeled shoes! She should have stayed with her jeans and clogs. Until now there had been several rows of people to serve as a buffer between them, but up close, his look was almost tangible. It was as if warm rays from his eyes were reaching out to touch her. Her sensitive body responded mindlessly as a flower turns toward the warmth of the sun.

Julia assumed a markedly ingenuous pose, a slight smile playing on her lips. "You forget, Brandon dear, that justice is portrayed as a blindfolded woman. And someday, I promise you, I'll get even for this evening."

He was far from being disturbed by Julia's cutting remarks, Melissa noticed. His gray-blue eyes lighted with what appeared to be a mixture of amusement and grudging respect. "You're your father's daughter, I must say. Tactful yet eloquently tenacious."

"Thank you." Julia nodded her head slightly. "Brandon, I'd like you to meet . . ."

As if suddenly aware of the interested circle of students that had gathered around them, who were obviously enjoying this impromptu interchange, Brandon cut off Julia's attempt at introductions.

"Let's get out of here," he said in a low voice. "Will you join me at my hotel for dinner?"

"Why not?" Julia answered. Melissa wondered for a brief moment if he were speaking to her as well, but she was not left long in doubt. The powerfully built lawyer stepped between her and Julia, took each by the arm, and rapidly propelled them down the remainder of the steps, out of the room, and into the corridor.

His decisive action served to eliminate any further discussion with the students who had stepped forward hoping to engage him in conversation. Embarrassed by their speculative looks as they dropped back, imperiously dismissed by the arrogant man, Melissa railed silently though she made no move to free herself from his firm grip.

She hadn't imagined his mere touch would be so electrifying. Angry with him for his condescending presumption that she'd be free for the evening, she rebelled at the command Brandon Kade had assumed over her. Yet she felt vague, nameless feminine stirrings she had not felt in years—not since Sonny's death, a few weeks before Jana's birth. It had been as though her sexuality had drained from her body upon hearing the news of the seaplane crash. She'd been in a state of sexual suspended animation—until now. Although outwardly composed, she frequently felt confused and full of conflicting impulses. She was acutely aware of Brandon Kade's tall figure looming above them as he swept them down the hall, out the door, into the damp dusk of the evening.

"Where's your car?" Brandon asked Julia, as they stood on the portico looking across the lamplit campus studded with flowering trees. The steady blowing rain had driven many of the pastel petals from their branches, strewing the walkways with wet pink and white confetti.

Julia pointed toward her sports coupe with the tip of the umbrella she'd started to open. Brandon held out his strong tanned hand for the keys, which Julia obediently gave him. Melissa was aware of the subtle musky scent of his masculine cologne as he bent his tall form, putting his arm around their shoulders. All three crowded together under the umbrella, dashing through the rain down the path under the natural arch formed by the trees lining the walk. It was strange how easily her body fitted against the hard leanness of his in the closeness of his protective embrace.

Julia held the umbrella over their heads as Brandon unlocked the door; then he took it from her, as the two women got into the car. Closing the umbrella with a snap before placing it on the floor behind Melissa's seat, he said, "Wait here until I get my car, and then follow me. We're going to the Alkai."

A moment later he drove past them honking his horn, and Julia wheeled out behind him. Silently intent, concentrating on maneuvering the silver-colored sports car through the heavy traffic of the rain-slick city streets, Julia hardly said a word, and Melissa was too preoccupied with her own disturbing thoughts to engage in casual conversation. How was it possible, Melissa wondered, to be so strongly drawn to a man who didn't even know her name?

She was startled when Julia suddenly broke the silence. "Follow me," she mimicked derisively. "Does he seriously think we couldn't find the Alkai without him?"

"Probably. He doesn't seem to have much respect for women's judgment," Melissa remarked.

Julia gave an uncharacteristic hoot of laughter. "You ought to *hear* what he has to say in private about women judges!"

"I can imagine," Melissa muttered. "Male chauvinism may have been declared dead by the media, but it's alive and flourishing in that car ahead of us!"

"I hate to admit it," Julia mused thoughtfully, "but, I've always suspected that there's something primitively sensual about male chauvinism that makes a certain degree of it essential to the man-woman relationship. The idea is really very sexy on its most fundamental level. You know, strong man, weak woman . . . his protectiveness giving her the illusion that she's cherished, wanted . . . at least in the bedroom."

"Yes, I suppose I know what you mean," Melissa agreed. "I don't think role reversal or the elimination of traditional male and female roles is necessary or even desirable for women to gain equality and respect. What happens today between a loving man and woman is as old as Adam and

Eve. But male chauvinism has no place at all outside the bedroom."

"Brandon'll come around in time. I intend to see to it," Julia promised. "One day, in the very near future, I have every intention of becoming an associate in Mr. Kade's law firm . . . though he doesn't know it yet." Melissa caught Julia's sly smile in the darkness of the car's interior. "One of the reasons I backed off in the seminar is that at the moment I feel sorry for him."

"You mean because of the divorce?"

"Yes, he's more than a little down on women right now, and with good reason. Remind me, and I'll tell you the background of that one sometime," Julia offered.

Melissa wondered what Julia could possibly have to tell, beyond what had been splashed on the front cover of every tabloid in the country, concerning Brandon Kade's recent divorce from an aspiring young movie starlet. Her apprehension at the thought of spending the evening with him nervously mounted with each block they traveled.

CHAPTER TWO

Alone in his rented sedan, Brandon Kade drove mechanically, going with the flow on this rainy night, rather than actively maneuvering through the slow-moving traffic in his customary aggressive style of driving. Several times he reached out instinctively for the shift stick as if he were in his own Jaguar, only to find himself groping in empty space. He was preoccupied, replaying the events of the past two hours in his mind.

Fortunately Burke had provided him with a roster of the students who were attending the seminar, so at least he knew her name. The clear blue of Melissa Collins Bennett's intelligent eyes dominated his consciousness; they shone out from a sweetly unaffected face that seemed full of honesty and tender vulnerability.

How different Melissa appeared from the women he was used to. Her natural beauty had been like a breath of fresh air to a man surfeited with vain, self-centered women whose only purpose in life seemed to be to draw attention to themselves.

From the moment he'd seen her seated by Julia in that lecture hall, Melissa's delicate uniqueness had captured his imagination. Now his mind groped: groped among flashy images of the varnished sophisticates who filled his circle of acquaintances, past them to the casual swingers met in bars and parties during his days as an air force pilot. His thoughts searched still further back to an earlier time, a time he rarely allowed himself to remember. Specters of the care-worn women of his Appalachian mountain childhood unhappily filled his mind's eye. He was groping, trying to identify the familiar chord of recognition Melissa struck within his heart.

As a courtroom lawyer he'd become accustomed to female witnesses assuming guileless, innocent disguises on the stand, only to break down when his relentless grilling exposed their true personalities and motivations. Was it possible that Melissa could be anything like she appeared, he wondered, as he braked for a yellow light he would have slipped through if he hadn't known the girls were behind him.

There was only one woman who seemed in any way like Melissa, Brandon slowly realized as he sat at the intersection. Grace Raymond's face came into sharp focus, but that notion was undoubtedly naïve, and certainly too good to be true. Grace Raymond, Julia's mother, the woman whom he admired most, had appeared much like Melissa in her younger days—the days in Philadelphia when she had first assumed the role of surrogate mother to her husband's young protégé.

As he mentally compared the two women, he realized there was little physical resemblance beyond their slight statures; however, a common aura of inbred refinement transcended the physical differences and seemed to unite the two in his mind. It was only with the Raymonds that he could drop his defenses and feel accepted as himself. Their seaside California estate was an oasis in an uncaring world, largely because of the warm atmosphere Grace Raymond created all around her.

A sharp honk from Julia's Supra brought him out of his reverie. Damn it! The light had changed from red to green without his realizing it. He had no patience for people who sat through lights, and here he was displaying the same lack of concentration. He could almost see the smirk of satisfaction that little oversight had brought to Julia's face.

As he firmly pressed down on the accelerator the car's wheels spun ineffectually on the wet pavement. Damn it! He'd provided another little amusement for Julia. Finally starting off at a moderate pace, he vaguely remembered Julia mentioning her roommate, Melissa, at some family gathering or another. It had been obvious both Warren and Grace were favorably impressed with the young woman, but he hadn't had reason to give her a second thought—until now.

This afternoon it had been difficult for him to keep his eyes off her as he'd lectured. He hoped his fascination hadn't been apparent to everyone around them. Something in her manner led him to suspect that a strong spirit lay just beneath Melissa's quiet, well-controlled demeanor.

He'd planned to work through the dinner hour—until the moment he'd stepped into the lecture hall and found his eyes drawn to the glowing blonde sitting in the third row, second seat from the left. Forcing restraint, he'd casually surveyed the room, student by student, row by row, until at last he'd allowed himself the indulgence of gazing at her freely. It had been a long time since he'd seen anyone blush, he thought cynically, but Melissa's blush had seemed genuine and was certainly becoming.

His evening's plans had changed quickly when he'd seized the opportunity to include Melissa in the surprise he had waiting for Julia. Inexplicably, it had become important to spend the few remaining hours he had left in Seattle with this enticing, enigmatic woman. He congratulated himself on engineering his invitation in a manner both Julia and Melissa would have found difficult to resist. He wouldn't have bet on his chances if he'd simply issued a conventional invitation and had waited for a reply. It hadn't escaped his notice that his views on the role of women in the legal profession had met with *both* young women's disfavor—to put it mildly.

Shifting uneasily in the seat, he became aware of a vague dissatisfaction gradually settling over him. It was as though he'd spent his thirty-eight years missing out on something vitally important, although at the moment he couldn't put into words what it was. A rising sense of excitement grew within him as he pulled into the venerable hotel's drive. He felt a curious, uncharacteristic need to explain himself, to justify himself to this petite woman he didn't even know.

Now hold it, buddy, not so fast; come to your senses, he warned himself harshly. You haven't even spoken with this woman; yet you're fantasizing like a love-sick school boy. You've just been burned, fella; the blisters haven't even healed yet. You sure didn't use any of the good judgment that's been your claim to fame when you marched up the aisle the first time. Here you are again, smart boy, attributing any number of glowing attributes to a ball of fluff you've yet to meet. Get out some of those tactics you're so proud of in the courtroom and find out what this little lady's all about, he determinedly advised himself as he stepped from the car.

Brandon, who had pulled to a stop in front of them, managed to reach Melissa's door just as the attendant opened Julia's. Melissa was acutely aware of the lawyer's appraising gaze on her slim legs as she swung them down to stand beside him. She felt his large hand cup her elbow possessively, as if to proclaim them a couple for the evening. Julia didn't seem to notice his action, although this slight hint of intimacy caused Melissa's heart to race absurdly.

As they walked across the well-lighted, mirrored lobby, Melissa noticed the elegant restorations of the landmark hotel. She admired the rich carving of the wide wooden moldings and the thick, deeply textured velvets that upholstered the charming antique furniture. She remembered reading that most of the furnishings had been brought around the Horn by early settlers at the beginning of the century and had been purchased by the hotel or donated from private collections. They certainly added authenticity, she noted, making this fine old structure a monument to the auspicious beginnings of the now flourishing metropolis of Seattle.

Since the hotel's reopening several weeks before, its restaurants and lounges had become popular night spots. The number of people waiting in the foyer for tables confirmed the report she'd heard that it was almost impossible even to get in. Apparently undaunted, Brandon escorted them past the reservation desk and directly into the main dining room.

The maître d'hôtel, a wide smile on his thinly moustached face, immediately led them toward a table where Scott, Julia's tall blond fiancé, leaped to his feet.

"Scott, I had no idea you were here!" Julia gasped, throwing herself into his open arms. "Brandon, why didn't you tell me? How could you do this to me?"

Melissa heard Brandon's chuckle close to her ear. "It seems I can't do anything to satisfy Miss Raymond today."

Melissa's skin tingled where his warm, pleasant breath touched her cheek. She stood clutching her handbag, vividly aware that Brandon had not released his grip on her elbow, as Scott explained his presence to his fiancée.

"I didn't tell you because I wasn't sure there'd be any time for us to get together. But when things cleared up a bit this afternoon, Brandon promised to bring you back to have dinner with me. I knew you'd be in classes all day and then at the seminar. Brandon and I will be taking off in just a few hours," he added ruefully.

During this exchange, Brandon's hand released Melissa's elbow and slid across her back to her opposite shoulder, pulling her closer to him, as if to draw her into his conspiracy. She knew she should resist his touch, but the sensation was so delicious that her traitorous body was compliant, still, in his embrace.

"You mean to say you knew you were coming and you didn't even tell me? When did you arrive?" Julia asked, pulling away from Scott, irritation replacing excitement.

"I only arrived this morning and we've been in consultation all day long. Brandon needed some confidential papers flown up. You know I wouldn't have left town without at least calling you, honey."

As Scott reassured Julia with a soft kiss, Melissa felt Brandon's strong hand squeeze her shoulder. She barely resisted an impulse to look up into his face.

"Brandon! You could have told me after the lecture. You make me so angry sometimes," Julia spluttered.

"He didn't tell you," Scott interjected hastily, "because he wanted to surprise you. Actually anyone in the office could have brought the papers, but since you were here, he had me come. That way, if it worked out all right, I'd have a chance to be with you a little while. So, you see"—he drew her back into his arms—"he was only thinking of us. Still angry with him?"

"Of course not." Placated, Julia smiled into her fiancé's eyes before turning her appreciative gaze on Brandon.

Melissa silently questioned whether thoughtfulness or the desire to manipulate the lives of others had caused Brandon Kade to arrange this little scene. In all the time since they'd left the university Melissa had been mentally sorting out the varying impressions she was getting about this man. She'd just seen him hold an entire roomful of people captive with his eloquence and compellingly forceful personality. At the same time she felt an element of arrogance and conceit in his commanding ability to make people do as he wished. She was almost afraid of him—afraid she might fall under his charming spell. As long as he didn't speak to her, nor she to him, she felt somewhat safe, though her skin blazed under the casual weight of his hand on her shoulder.

"I'm vindicated then, Miss Raymond?" Brandon teased.

"On this one point," Julia conceded.

"If I ever find myself in a jam and need a good defense attorney, Scott, you're my man," Brandon said jokingly. "Would I hear any objections if I suggested that the four of us sit down?" he went on in the same tone. "Standing here, we seem to be drawing considerable attention. I'd rather not be part of the floor show, if you don't mind."

A quick glance affirmed Brandon's observation. Melissa took in the varying degrees of discretion with which a good number of the restaurant's patrons were looking at them. The women's eyes were indiscreetly directed toward Brandon Kade, she noted without surprise. He was unquestionably as handsome a man as one would ever be likely to see, and catching a glimpse of envy directed toward her, she realized with a flush of embarrassment that he still had his arm around her as though they had come together.

Releasing her, Brandon pulled out the high-backed, richly upholstered chair for Melissa and politely helped her remove her jacket before seating himself at her side. She forced herself not to react to his maddening touch in any outward manner.

"I don't believe we've been introduced," he remarked, his steel-blue eyes engaging Melissa's. "Three years in law school appear to have taken the polish off Julia's finishing school manners," he taunted lightly.

"You haven't given me the time or opportunity to introduce her," Julia interjected in her own defense, her wide mouth pouting. "Melissa, I'd like you to meet, formally that is"—Julia glared as she carefully enunciated his name—"Brandon Kade. Brandon, this is Melissa Bennett, my roommate and best friend. She's to be matron of honor at my wedding."

"I'm pleased to meet you, Melissa. Can you talk?" he asked, his gray-blue eyes sparkling wickedly. Then he quickly made amends, adding, "Forgive me, that was unpardonably rude. Sometimes I forget that Julia's grown-up now and her friends are too. I'm sure it's just that still waters run deep."

His warm smile caused Melissa's heart to lurch. Far from insulting her, his familiar teasing banter made her feel that he easily accepted her as an integral part of Julia's life. In his brotherly relationship to Julia, he was already treating her as a personal friend—not as a tagalong. She could see now he'd adroitly planned to include her in their group from the first. Confused and uncertain, absurdly she began to wonder what her life had been like before she'd met him and what it would be like after he had gone.

"We haven't given her a chance to say anything," Julia pointed out archly.

"I know. So now it's her turn," Brandon said, his eyes on Melissa.

She racked her brain for some witty impressive rejoinder, but her mind was so filled with conflicting emotions she didn't know how to begin. Yet she felt compelled to say something. Good heavens, she thought with dismay, was this the way she would react in a court of law when she came face to face with a sexually attractive opponent? Tongue-tied and inarticulate? No! She refused to accept that. She'd been on a winning debate team in high school and had actually excelled in public speaking ever since, in spite of a natural personal reticence. She knew she could come up against anyone . . . as long as it wasn't Brandon Kade!

When a cocktail waitress appeared at their table, Brandon asked Melissa, "Would you like something to drink?"

"No, thank you," she answered demurely, feeling in desperate need of all her wits.

"No?" His knowing smile increased her discomfort, convincing her she'd confirmed her status as an unsophisticated bumpkin in his worldly eyes.

He turned to Julia and Scott. "How about you two?"

"A glass of white wine would be nice," Julia replied.

"That's fine with me too," Scott agreed.

"I think I'll wait until dinner," Brandon said, as he smiled charmingly at the waitress. "On second thought"—he raised an immaculately groomed hand to halt her departure—"I'll have Perrier with a twist of lime."

When the waitress left, Brandon turned back to Melissa. She knew she had to say something now. Every moment that passed would only make it more difficult. She kept her hands in her lap, resisting the impulse to touch her flushed cheek, aware she had the full attention of all three. How had she ended up in the limelight?

The topic of the weather flashed briefly through her mind, before she discounted it as hopelessly mundane. If only she could think of something sparkling and clever!

"Have you been in Seattle before?" she heard herself ask inanely, knowing full well that he had.

What she wanted to say was, Stop looking at me! Stop undermining the very foundations on which I've been carefully constructing my life. Stop threatening my independence and my resolve!

"Yes, I've been here several times," he said in mock seriousness, his eyes glinting with humor. "And now that we've established that important fact, let's get a little more personal. Tell me why such an attractive young woman is spending her life in law school. You don't look old enough to vote, let alone to be graduating cum laude."

Startled, she asked, "How did you know that?" Now it was her blue eyes that confronted his.

"My old friend Eric Burke supplied me with a few details. With only two women qualified to attend the seminar, naturally I was curious about you. I already knew all about Julia, of course," he said with a wink, leaning back comfortably in his seat. "Burke also told me you have a small daughter and that you're going to be a corporate attorney for your father-in-law in Alaska. If that's the case, why the interest in criminal law, Snowbird?" He looked at her with keen interest on his intelligent face.

Snowbird? Had he forgotten her name? "I've always been interested in defending people who need help," Melissa replied honestly. Distracted by his air of familiarity and impromptu use of a nickname for her, she didn't add that his flamboyant example had helped form that aspiration.

"It's a tough business," he remarked cynically. The line of his face hardened as he looked down, languidly swirling the lime peel in his glass. "It takes a lot out of you. The incidence of burnout is significantly greater among trial lawyers than in other legal fields."

"Does that bother *you?*" she shot back.

"Not in the least," he replied without hesitation.

"Then why do you assume it would be a deterrent to me?" she asked, meeting his eyes levelly, quite sure of his reply.

"Because you're a woman," he said evenly, as though that were the answer to any question she might ask.

Remembering her resolve to stay as unemotional as possible, she took a deep breath, mentally making herself count to ten before answering. Finally she said, "And because I'm a woman I'm not supposed to know how the world runs or to have any hand in running it? Do you think that I'm biologically inferior in some way?" Melissa felt her discomfort grow while he withheld his reply. Annoyed, she stoically tolerated his ploy as he took a sip of sparkling water.

"Absolutely not," he drawled at last, flashing her a maddeningly charming smile. "You're biologically fine—even superior, I would venture to guess." His eyes boldly ran over the curves of her breasts clearly outlined in her sheer blouse.

Inwardly furious, Melissa silently chastised herself, once more aware of her body's betrayal as her cheeks flared to an incriminating flush. I walked right into that one, she thought. After hearing everything he's said to Julia all evening, I should have known better. She almost wished she'd ordered a double martini earlier when she'd had the chance. In fact, she idly wondered how many martinis it would take before she could slide gracefully under the table.

"And as for having a hand in how the world runs, there's an old saying that 'the hand that rocks the cradle is the one that rules the world.' " Brandon pompously finished with infuriating smugness, before raising his glass again to his lips.

"Which brings us back to where we were earlier," Julia interjected. "I'm surprised you find yourself at such a loss for original ideas that you have to resort to outmoded clichés and maxims," she said sarcastically.

Her fiancé rolled his eyes and softly groaned at the manner in which his intended wife was taking his boss to task. Brandon remained unperturbed, the glint of humor never leaving his eyes.

Julia turned to Melissa. "We'll never get anywhere arguing with him. He's a practicing chauvinist and loves to upset women. I think he does it on purpose to make himself feel more macho." She simpered with counterfeit sweetness as she made the barbed remark.

Melissa clenched her teeth. Ordinarily an easy conversationalist, she had been at a loss for words all evening. I've been almost speechless ever since I saw him at the seminar, she thought. The first stupid remark I did make was totally put down and Julia had to step in to save me. He must think I'm an idiot!

"Brandon, are you going fishing with Dad this summer? I believe I remember Mother telling me that when she called." Julia had come to her rescue once more by changing the subject. "My father has an open session this summer," she explained to Melissa. "I'm glad, because otherwise it would make it very difficult with the wedding. And he really needs a rest."

"Yes, I'm joining your dad as soon as the case I'm on now is finished," Brandon replied. "I'm looking forward to it. I haven't been out with him for over a year. Although I enjoy deep-sea fishing, and the chance to relax, you know that I go for his company more than anything.

"The judge is a great guy and over the years he's taught me practically everything I know about courtroom behavior. If you're really serious about law," he said patronizingly, "you girls could learn a great deal from him. He's one of the best. He can see through the deviousness of attorneys and witnesses alike. Any person who comes before his bench can be sure of a fair trial and an honest, impartial judgment based on the facts. I can't say that about every judge I've argued before." He gave a short disparaging laugh.

Julia beamed with pride. Melissa knew how proud she was of her father and it was evident Julia felt he'd been paid a supreme compliment.

Scott diplomatically took the opportunity to break into the conversation while it was on an even keel. "We take off at eleven o'clock." He looked into Julia's smoky gray eyes. "Actually I'm not very hungry . . ."

Julia immediately took the cue and picked up her clutch bag. "I'm not either."

"Would you two mind very much if we skipped dinner and took a walk . . . or something?" Scott said. Then he added, to Brandon, "I can see Julia to her apartment and meet you at the plane at eleven."

"Oh, we don't mind at all." Brandon rose from his chair as Julia stood. "Sounds like a good idea . . . especially the 'or something,' " he laughed. "I'll be happy to take Melissa home later after we've had dinner."

He did remember her name, Melissa thought with fleeting pleasure in the moment before the reality of the situation hit her.

"Alone at last," Brandon said in an intimate tantalizing tone. Seating himself, he offhandedly put his arm around the back of her chair. His fingertips lightly brushing her shoulder through her sheer blouse sparked an unbidden deeply feminine response.

Melissa's eyes widened in disbelief. It had all happened so quickly that she hadn't had time to protest. Momentarily shocked that Julia could desert her so easily, she straightened in her chair, conspicuously moving away from the seductive warmth of his hand. But then what could she have said? That she wanted the engaged couple to take her with them? What could have been more ridiculous than that? She would never deprive Julia of an opportunity to be alone with Scott. Yet she felt like an innocent lamb being left for the sacrifice. Uncomfortable with the unmistakable signs of the beginnings of a foolhardy infatuation, she felt deserted, left to a fate she might not be able to control. What defenses did her heart have against a casual assault by this overwhelmingly attractive, charming man? His slightest touch had been enough to make her knees go weak.

"I understand love does strange things to one's appetite," was Brandon's wry comment. "Though I can't say I've ever had that problem," he continued with a smile, leaning toward her in an easy confidential manner, clearly intending to start their conversation on a very personal level. "Have you?"

What kind of response did he expect her to make to that highly leading, impertinent question? Melissa moved still further away from him. After all, he'd been married—very *much* married—and to a beautiful, desirable woman. She refused to be drawn into an intimate conversation concerning his love life . . . or hers!

What was she doing in this sophisticated night spot sitting next to one of the most polished, urbane men in the country? It'd been a long time since she'd had to pull out her social graces, but they couldn't have all been lost in that musty law library. However capriciously she'd arrived here, here she was and she'd do her damnedest to play out her role. Inwardly she resolved that she would not permit him to overcome her with the force of his personality.

"Do you cross-examine all lawyers of your acquaintance about their love lives and offer confidential details of yours?" she queried lightly.

"Only if they're young and beautiful with clear blue eyes . . . and most importantly, female," he countered.

Acknowledging the compliment inherent in this remark,

she smiled sweetly. "I don't know about you," she said with cool deliberation, intended to show him that his flirtatious attentions had left her unaffected, "but I'm famished. I believe you invited me to dinner, Brandon." She forced herself to use his first name casually. "Perhaps we should look at a menu." Her calm was a concerted effort to disguise the havoc his sensuous charm had already wrought upon her appetite.

"Of course, Melissa," he said, smiling and playing right along with her. He still clearly viewed her with an amused air of superiority.

Brandon gestured slightly for the waiter, who instantly came to the table with two large leather-bound folders. The wine steward immediately followed and handed Brandon a thicker, similarly bound wine list.

At a glance Melissa noted that the menu was strictly a la carte and its prices absolutely astronomical. She studied the offerings with pretended absorption until, disturbed by a feeling that she was being watched, she looked up to encounter rapt interest on Brandon's handsome face as he openly studied her instead of the wine list he held. With a coolness she didn't feel, she pulled her gaze from his and turned back to the menu. She made up her mind, though she wasn't even slightly hungry, to order the most elaborate, expensive meal she could choose. Mentally she breathed a tribute of thanks to her father-in-law for preparing her for this moment. Although a man of few cultural interests, he had a highly developed appreciation for fine foods and vintage wines.

Pondering the menu a moment longer, balancing her choices for their varied textures and colors, she spoke. "I'm ready to order."

"Fine," he answered. "What would you like?"

Did she discern a slight twinkle of condescension in his expressive eyes? Did he think she wasn't equal to the task? Well, he was in for a surprise. Mr. Kade would soon find out she had *some* sophistication.

"I'd like to start with the wild pheasant liver pâté with truffles, and with it I'd like a good Beaujolais, let's say a '61." Unfortunately, the pâté was not the most expensive appetizer on the menu, but she'd never cultivated a taste for snails, so escargots were definitely out. "To follow, I'd like lobster in aspic with a very light Chablis."

With that, Brandon closed the wine list and placed it on the table beside him. She noticed with satisfaction that the twinkle had left his eyes as he opened his menu to follow her selections.

"For my entrée I think roast duck with a salad en brochette of avocado and artichokes would be nice. Pinot Noir will go well with that." She closed her menu and deliberately placed it on top of the discarded wine list. Relaxing in his presence for the first time, she was content that the expertise with which she'd ordered the meal without even consulting the wine list had to have made a favorable impression on him.

"No champagne?" he asked with feigned innocence.

"Of course," she answered sweetly. "With dessert." Really! Did he expect to catch her in a blunder as gauche as that?

"Obviously *you're* not in love," he observed dryly, resting his elbows comfortably on the arms of the chair. "Everything you've selected sounds perfect to me. Compatible, aren't we?" Admiration showed in his eyes as his smile widened.

Given free rein, her wayward emotions could easily lead her down a dangerous path. At this point there was no way she could complicate her life further with any man, let alone this one. Besides, Melissa's reason warned that Brandon Kade's interest in her went no farther than an idle evening's diversion. In fact, he'd been toying with her ever since he walked into that lecture hall. It was as if she were no more than a windup doll perched precariously on a shelf in a toy store, awaiting the manipulations of his touch to come to life, doomed to be discarded when a flashier toy caught his eye. But she was not his plaything, nor did she intend to become so—no matter how tempting the idea might be.

CHAPTER THREE

She's put me in my place, Brandon thought with appreciative amusement, and she's done it with class. He admired the wit and humor she'd displayed by ordering the most expensive items on the menu, as if to demonstrate the best was none too good for her. He was rapidly becoming convinced that that was very likely the case, and he had to admit he'd have been vastly disappointed had she done anything less. It was sound evidence that he'd begun to uncover the personal qualities that he'd suspected lay hidden just below that beautiful, calm exterior.

Even more entertaining had been the audacious way she'd usurped his male prerogative by superbly selecting the appropriate wines to accompany each course. Peculiarly, the feminist tendencies she displayed, which would have turned him off in any other woman, only enhanced the fascination she held for him. Oh, yes, Melissa Collins Bennett had played her cards like a pro, but inadvertently she'd shown the weakness in her hand. Obviously the little lady had an aversion to escargots. They were substantially more expensive than the pâté, and he knew that she hadn't simply overlooked that fact. He could *not* resist trumping her ace.

Brandon closed his menu and settled back in his chair, an irritatingly smug smile on his lips, as the waiter and wine steward immediately appeared at his side. Something in his look made Melissa decidedly uncomfortable.

"We'll start with the pâté and truffles and a 1961 Beaujolais . . . and also an order of escargots. It appears to be your finest appetizer, and we mustn't miss that, must we, Melissa?" His wicked smile told it all—he'd caught onto her game and with his celebrated acuteness had mercilessly found her vulnerable spot.

"Certainly not," she replied evenly, although the thought of gagging down even one of those repulsive, garlic-buttered, black, rubbery snails made her stomach churn. "I don't know how I missed that."

It would have been easy to simply have told him she didn't care for snails. Too easy. In doing so she would have lost her advantage. He'd taken that trick, but with finesse she could still win this hand. He was quick on the uptake, no question of that. The most she could hope for was that he didn't like snails either. She knew instinctively that wouldn't serve as the slightest deterrent to his ordering the nasty little things. Perhaps if he didn't like them, their meal would be reduced to a duel with tongs and cocktail forks! If so, she wouldn't surrender first. She vowed silently that she'd manage to choke down one of the little creatures no matter what the gastronomical results might be! Despite her distress, she was somehow perversely pleased that he'd understood her tactics and had effectively countered them. With a rising sense of excitement she acknowledged that it was fun to play a game with a worthy opponent. She wasn't about to throw in her hand until the last trump was played.

As Brandon competently ordered the meal, she observed him from beneath thick lashes. She'd seen his face in photographs many times: in newspapers, on the pages of national weekly news magazines, and on the front of sensational tabloids. In fact, she was quite sure she still had the issue of a magazine in which he had been featured as "most notable man of the year." Having thought herself well prepared for his appearance—that he was movie-star handsome was not a surprise—she still experienced a sense of shock as she realized all the photographs had failed to capture the force of personality and intellect that combined with great good looks to make Brandon Kade the most attractive man she'd ever seen—and, unfortunately, the most unattainable.

The task of ordering completed, Brandon turned his attention back to Melissa. His voice was honeyed and low. "To rephrase my question, which you pointedly avoided and to which I'd very much like an answer: are you in love with anyone?"

"I hardly think this is the time or place to discuss that." Melissa reddened, privately wondering if she could honestly answer his provocative question at this moment. She hadn't been in love only hours ago . . . but now?

"What do you think is going on all around us?" His hand, wholly masculine with a light sprinkling of black hairs, gestured in a leisurely circle encompassing the candlelit tables accommodating well-dressed, handsome people engaged in absorbing conversation.

She had to admit that dining out was an integral part of the rites of love. Food and drink played an important role in the ritual of courtship and in the renewal of long-term loving relationships.

"But we hardly know each other," she protested, suddenly unwilling to admit to the celibate existence of her past few years.

"That's the situation I'm trying to remedy." He grinned devilishly. "But if you won't cooperate and talk about love, then we'll have to resort to the second most common subject of dinner conversation: business. Much duller, but it's still a chance to learn about you." His words were intoxicatingly, druggingly suave. "So I'll reiterate another unanswered question of mine: why are you so set on corporate law when you admit criminal law would be your first choice?"

At least she had a reasonable answer to this question, one that anchored her to reality and kept her body and soul, stimulated by his warm attentive nearness, from soaring off on a flight of frenzied fancy.

"I'm going to be a practicing corporate attorney out of family loyalty," she stated flatly, jutting out her well-formed chin.

"Family loyalty?" He frowned, pushing his chair back slightly to look at her squarely. "To whom?"

"My father-in-law. I owe him a great deal. He and my daughter are all I have. He's been wonderful. He's stood by me through everything." Melissa felt uncomfortable and on the defensive, yet she continued her explanation. "I know what it is to be an orphan . . . and a widow. I'm not about to cut myself off from Dad or to deprive Jana of the opportunity to grow up knowing and loving her grandfather. He needs us."

"You're going to base your entire future on that?" Well-formed black brows raised incredulously.

"Yes, I am," she said. "At least to a certain degree," she amended, inwardly aware that she was going to assert her independence within the framework of her love for her father-in-law. "Don't you feel any family loyalty or responsibility?"

He snorted. "If I believed that family loyalty should dictate what one does with his life, I'd be an unemployed coal miner playing video games and buying moonshine with quarters I could ill afford to squander. I certainly wouldn't be sitting in this restaurant with a beautiful woman who wants to discuss family loyalty. I'm where I am in spite of my family—not because of them!" His eyes flashed in the candle glow. "I owe my family nothing . . . absolutely nothing!"

A hint of bitterness twisted his mouth. Melissa could sense a depth of unresolved conflict hidden beneath his polished veneer. He'd seemed untouched, invulnerable until now. In a moment Brandon Kade became to her more than an image, much more. He became a real man capable of hurting and being hurt, capable of loving and being loved. Her heart went out to him.

In an effort to dispel the sadness in his eyes, she raised her wineglass. "It's a long way from homemade moonshine to this." Her comment was intended to lighten the mood.

A smile softened his guarded expression. "Longer than you'll ever know."

"How *did* you make it?" she asked, recalling that his impassioned speech had been about class warfare and social injustice. Obviously the topic hadn't been merely altruistic rhetoric, slickly used to justify his lucrative accomplishments. The issue was so personal that the slightest reference to his background exposed a raw nerve.

"By taking a case no one else would touch my first year out of law school. I went out on a limb. Even got fired from a coveted position in a prestigious New York law firm for doing it."

"What kind of case could have possibly been worth that to you?"

"It's not an appetizing source of dinner conversation," he warned.

"Please. I'm very interested." She felt an inexplicable tension. Perhaps here was an area where they could reach a common ground of understanding. Melissa was filled with curiosity about his motives for having done something so rash. The case couldn't have been trivial—there was nothing trivial about this disturbing man.

"A young working-class girl was raped and murdered in Central Park. Angered by the authorities' lack of action, convinced that justice would never be done, the mother took the law in her own hands and shot the young man she was sure was the murderer. When she appealed for legal assistance, my firm refused to defend her, acting as though the case against her was open and shut. I happened to find out that the young man's socially prominent family were intimate friends with one of the senior partners. Everyone wanted the whole matter hushed up and forgotten with as little publicity as possible."

He stopped. "Do you really want to hear all the lurid details about my illustrious climb to fame?" he joked.

"Absolutely," Melissa replied without blinking, realizing that all this must have happened before she'd even developed an interest in law. For the first time she felt an empathy growing between them.

"I was young and brash. Straight out of law school, I held strong moral convictions and could see social injustice rearing its ugly head around every corner. I couldn't resist going to interview the woman myself. The effect she had on me was amazing. She was so calm." He shook his dark head disbelievingly. "So accepting of her fate. You see, she truly believed her daughter's murderer would have been exonerated in court because of his social standing. In her mind her action was the only path to justice. I couldn't walk away from her."

"Even though it meant putting your career on the line?" Melissa's eyes appraised him, seeing a depth of character the media had never portrayed. She could have dealt with superficiality, arrogance, and opportunism, but her heart wasn't prepared to resist the appeal of this absolute selflessness.

"I knew I could never obtain a "not guilty" verdict, but I figured that if I could prove the young man's guilt the bereaved mother would receive a far less serious sentence. After making my decision to defend her known, I found myself out on the street, a law firm of one."

"What happened then?"

"It was a long trial, but fortunately I had a sympathetic jury and a judge with daughters of his own. The woman received the lightest sentence possible."

"You're far too modest, I'm sure, Mr. Kade." Melissa's eyes sparkled, thinking of the dedication and brilliant legal maneuvering it must have taken for a novice trial lawyer to pull that off. "It couldn't have been that easy."

"You think not, Mrs. Bennett?" he asked wryly.

"I think not, Mr. Kade," she agreed. They broke into

mutual laughter. "Even though you won the case I would have thought bucking the system would have ruined your career."

"It easily could have," he admitted, a hint of appreciation for her insight lighting his features, "but I had two powerful influences backing me. The press was one. Because of the sensational nature of the case it caught the public's interest, and the story went nationwide. Before I knew it I found my face staring at me from every newsstand and there was a reporter jumping out from behind every courtroom door to stick a microphone under my nose." He chuckled.

Melissa could readily understand why that had happened. She found herself stirred by the very sound of his voice, moved by the chiseled line of his masculine profile. The vibrantly handsome young man with the courage of his convictions had flamed the interest of a celebrity-happy country. Photogenic and articulate, he'd been good copy ever since.

"And the other backer?" she asked.

"Judge Raymond, Julia's father. He'd been my mentor and friend for years. It was he who suggested I make a fresh start in San Francisco, knowing I didn't have a chance left with the eastern establishment. It was a good move, and all the publicity helped. After the first trial my services were in great demand. I've had more than I could handle ever since." He exuded an air of calm self-assurance.

"You've known the Raymonds since Julia was a child, haven't you?" Melissa asked, feeling pleasantly relaxed.

"Yes, and I can't make myself believe she's old enough to be getting married. I'm pleased with her choice though. She's marrying a winner."

"They seem very much in love," Melissa agreed.

"Scott's definitely slated for success. After a year or two of wedded bliss, when she's given up her idea of a law career, Julia will be a real asset to him." This absurd notion was spoken authoritatively.

"What makes you think she has any intention of giving up

her law career?" Melissa demanded heatedly. What arrogance! Of course, how had she allowed a few moments of intimate conversation to distract her from the knowledge of what this man really was: a condescending egotist!

The waiter appeared and placed the dishes with their repulsive contents before them. Contemplating the snail shells, Melissa tried to remind herself that some people consider escargots a delicacy.

"There's never been any doubt in my mind. I've known her most of her life. She's too emotional to make a good trial lawyer. As much as I care for Julia, I've always felt it was a shame she wasn't a boy. The judge deserved someone to carry on his name and legislative heritage and talent."

"I can't believe in this day and age that anyone could say those things!" Hurt and humiliated to think that she'd ever shared any sympathy with this man, Melissa stared in open disbelief.

He met her angry remark coolly. His athletic body still at ease, his gaze became sharply focused. "Few women have the strength of will to dedicate their lives to a profession. Most who try to combine family and career end up doing neither very well, or end up dropping out of the competition. I've read some studies on that. It's a real social phenomenon. Look at you—you're a case in point. You've already compromised by letting someone decide the kind of law you'll practice. You'll see. I predict a desirable young woman like you will soon be married, contented with volunteer work and the country club scene."

A convulsive shiver shook her body. Even though for a few moments he'd seemed to treat her as an equal, even as a colleague whom he could respect, all she was in his eyes was a "mere woman." Brandon Kade might be intellectually brilliant, but he had a great deal to learn, and she didn't have the desire or patience to teach him. Her Irish dander, usually so well controlled that only her intimates even suspected its existence, seethed deep down inside like a newly awakening volcano. Bubbling up, its heat wiped out her feelings of humiliation and frustration, replacing them with molten anger.

Was she the more angry at him for his misguided, condescending opinions, or at herself for being fool enough to feel stirrings of passion for him within her heart? Either way it didn't matter. She had to get away from him and the threat he represented to her hard-fought dreams of independence. Dreams she intended to turn into reality, despite his damning predictions.

She rose hastily, her voice deep and throaty. "I'm leaving."

He was barely to his feet, an astonished look on his face, as she continued. "I apologize for my rudeness, something *you* probably won't understand. Eat your escargots and gloat! I hope you choke on every one of them." She snatched her jacket from the back of the chair and ran blindly from the room, oblivious to curious glances from other diners.

At the entrance to the hotel, she found the doorman. "Taxi, please," she requested, struggling into her jacket, looking over her shoulder, fearful that Brandon would follow.

"Sorry, ma'am. They're slow tonight because of the weather. Take a seat in the lobby and I'll do my best."

"I can't wait," she got out, before she plunged into the cold dark night.

Melissa hurried down the nearly deserted thoroughfare toward the far distant goal of her apartment set high on a twinkling hill above the city. Fear mounted with every step she took down the mist-shrouded street. The lonely sounds of her own echoing footsteps became in themselves a source of terror. Unconsciously, her stride accelerated from a rapid walk to a desperate run as though she were being pursued, her frightened heart exaggerating and magnifying the city noises into the shrieks of banshees.

She knew with growing terror that she shouldn't be out

alone on a city street. She'd hoped to find a place still open where she could call a taxi, but she passed only darkened storefronts and tightly locked office buildings. Penetrating rain quickly soaked through her thin woolen jacket; her open-toed shoes squished unpleasantly with every step; her hair hung in dripping strands about her face.

"Damn that insufferable egotist," she gasped aloud as Brandon's last words ran through her mind. "If it weren't for him and his intolerable conceit, I wouldn't be in this mess!" She berated herself for allowing his didactic words to dictate her foolhardy, dangerous course of action.

Haunting fear became stark reality. Three blocks from the hotel a large shadow moved out unexpectedly from an alley, lumbering directly into her path. A strong hand took hold of her upper arm.

The smell of liquor assaulted her nostrils as the figure before her demanded in a hoarse whisper, "Little lady, I need some money . . . now!"

Frantically, she tried to wrench herself free of the loathsome creature. His drunken stumble nearly dragged her to the pavement as he lurched to steady himself. A horrified scream tore from her throat as one unkempt hand fumbled across her breasts.

Suddenly the terrifying scene was illuminated in the brilliant blaze of headlights, cutting through the mist of fog and rain, as a car screeched to a halt beside them. Melissa felt herself being torn from the grasp of the attacker and held tightly against the familiar Aramis-scented comfort of Brandon Kade's hard masculine frame. The sound of footsteps hastily retreating into the dark alleyway assured her there would be no further trouble. She was sure that the derelict would have been no match for the athletic prowess of the man who now held her in his arms.

Trembling uncontrollably, her shaken body instinctively clung to the refuge of Brandon's embrace. Dimly, above the pounding of her heart she could hear him asking urgently over and over, "Are you all right? Did he hurt you, Melissa? Tell me, are you all right?" His words so tenderly spoken offered comforting solace . . . his arms a safe haven from the lurking dangers of the urban jungle.

Gradually her fear-stricken mind cleared to the realization that she was clinging to the very man she had been fleeing from. Although Brandon's attack had been verbal, it had been nonetheless as dangerous to her sense of well-being as had the physical attack of the vagrant. She renewed her struggle against this new threat to her self-esteem, sensing that his rescue graphically reaffirmed his conviction that she couldn't take care of herself in a man's world.

"Let me go," Melissa moaned as she ineffectively tried to release herself from the steel of his arms.

"Get in the car," he ordered gruffly, his voice changing from its former gentleness to the tone of command, "or I'll pick you up and put you in myself. You've no business alone on a street like this at night."

"I can take care of myself," she shouted, curling her hands into fists to pummel futilely against his muscular chest, at once realizing the ridiculousness of her statement.

Their struggling figures were parodied in larger-than-life shadows against the brick wall behind them. Humiliated by the pure physical superiority he held over her, Melissa felt her anger surge with impotent rage.

A police car, its bright blue light flashing, pulsating brilliantly in the night, pulled in front of Brandon's car, effectively blocking an easy exit.

"What's going on here?" a uniformed officer demanded as he jumped from the car, one hand resting lightly on the butt of a hip pistol. Another patrolman quickly joined him, having approached from the other side.

"Just a lovers' quarrel, Officer," Brandon offered smoothly. "The lady thinks she can walk home alone."

Melissa felt an instant bond of masculine understanding form between Brandon and the policemen as they took in his well-dressed presence and responded to the command of his person, which, to her fury, excluded her as a rational actor in this charade.

However, the officer proceeded dutifully, asking, "Is that true, ma'am? Do you want to go with this man?" She felt his eyes quizzically take in her rain-sodden appearance.

Any further display of antagonism would blow the entire situation out of proportion, Melissa realized, although the vengeful thought of having Brandon Kade arrested flickered through her mind. If it weren't for the strong sense of loyalty she felt to Julia and her family, she might do just that! After a moment of silence, while she stood rigidly contemplating her alternatives, she gave in. Her body went limp in the attorney's grip.

"Yes," she answered, allowing herself to be led to the passenger side of Brandon's rented car.

Brandon smilingly saluted the policemen before backing out into the street and heading in the direction of Queen Anne Hill.

The silence between them was palpable. My Lord, Melissa thought, what would have happened if he hadn't cared enough to come after me? How could she have been foolish enough to equate Brandon's verbal abuse with the attack of the vagrant? She should have stayed in that restaurant. Should have met him word for word instead of allowing her emotions to take control, hurtling her out into danger. Glancing sideways, she took in the broad-shouldered physique and well-shaped head of the man beside her. She might even owe him her life.

"Brandon," she said, breaking the taut silence, "thank you for coming after me."

"You don't owe me any thanks, Melissa," Brandon said contritely, much to her surprise. "I was just mentally kicking myself for putting you in that situation. You can berate me to your heart's content. Nothing you could say could ever equal the names I've been calling myself for exposing you to danger. I'm truly sorry.

"My God, what would have happened if I hadn't gotten to you in time?" he finished in anguish, unconsciously echoing her own thoughts.

The last thing Melissa expected was this open admission of responsibility and guilt from Brandon Kade. Her defenses crumbled.

Pulling the car over to the curb, leaving the motor running, he shifted in his seat so that he could look at her directly. "I owe you an apology for my remarks," he said with genuine sincerity. She waited for an explanation, but he offered none. Obviously he found apologizing difficult, but his darkened eyes spoke for him. There was a depth of tenderness she'd only glimpsed briefly before. A tenderness that took away the arrogant set of his face and softened the firm line of his mouth, curving his lips into a pleasing crescent.

Finally he went on, his deep voice a melodious murmur. "Will you give me a second chance?" When his hand reached over to cover hers, she didn't pull away. "Can we strike this episode from the record of our relationship, Counselor?" A slight familiar tone of teasing had entered his voice as he cocked his head down to look into her lowered eyes. "Could you even go so far as to pardon me?" He cupped her chin in his hand and raised her face, brushing back the wet strands of hair that fell across her forehead. The intensity of his gaze captured and held hers.

It would be senseless to argue with him, absolutely pointless, she told herself. Their relationship had no future—philosophically they were diametrically opposed. There was no need for bitterness or rancor—or any feeling at all, for that matter, she told her racing heart. It was over. All she wanted at this moment was to be safe and warm in her own apartment, to wipe the disturbing memories of this evening from her mind, and to rid herself of the unaccountable attraction this paradoxical man held for her.

"Case closed," was all she could trust herself to offer.

"Thank you." His voice was gentle as he raised her hand to his lips, causing a violent shiver to shake her small frame. "You're soaking wet. We've got to get you home," he said, pulling out onto the street.

The touch of his lips had dispelled her anger, toppling the last vestige of her defenses. Physically drained of fear and antagonism, tired from the strain of the evening, she felt another cold shiver wrack her body, causing Brandon to reach over and pull her closely to him. The touch of his cheek against her damp hair comforted her; the warmth of his body transmitted itself to hers.

Despite her exhaustion, during the short drive Melissa became aware of a surging sense of sexual excitement rising between them. The firm support of his arm as she leaned against him sent a power through her, charging her senses. It was as though his touch could control her heartbeat, quicken her breathing, stimulate her desire.

Arriving at Melissa's home, a stately old hillside house that had been converted into unique apartments, Melissa pulled away from Brandon and nervously opened the passenger door as soon as the car came to a stop.

"Wait, just a minute," Brandon said insistently as he turned off the engine. The hold of his strong hand on her slender shoulder tightened, pulling her back toward him.

Streetlight streamed down through the trees, creating fascinating shadows of light and dark around them. Melissa's slim body tensed with almost unendurable nervous excitement. Brandon easily turned her toward him, and in the silver glow of the elusive moon that now highlighted her face, he traced the outline of her soft cheek before allowing his finger to rest tantalizingly on her lips. She didn't resist his action. She couldn't deny the desire smoldering in the depths of his compelling eyes. Breath caught in her throat at his gentle touch. Sweet apprehension filled her being with a longing she'd almost forgotten.

A distinct seductive drawl was detectable in his deep, melodious voice as he said, "Do you have any idea how beautiful you are, Snowbird?" The lyrical cadence of his words fell liltingly on her ears, scarcely bearable.

Mesmerized, Melissa stared into his eyes as she welcomed the muscular arms that encircled her; expectantly waiting for the proud, firm mouth that sought her softly parted lips. Her spellbound body yielded to his physical and emotional demands as she surrendered all intellectual resistance.

He kissed her at first gently, with self-restraint, slowly, patiently arousing her slumbering sensuousness with lips moist and pliant. The pressure of his mouth became demanding; his insistent tongue dizzyingly invadingly explorative, as he increased the intensity of his embrace. Awareness of the pressing drive of his male urgency awakened her womanly flesh to the latent needs of her love-starved body, exciting her emotions as deeply as her flesh.

Her arm clung to the steel of his neck; her hand instinctively ran through his luxuriantly thick, black hair. As she responded fully to his commanding yet tender embrace, his passion quickened. A wild warmth raced throughout her body, heating her chilled form to the red-hot throbbing fire of desire. He drew her even closer—one soul-stirring kiss melding into another and still another and another. As his hands gently explored its slender contours, her aroused body strained against his, mindlessly begging for fulfillment. She wanted to be held in his arms forever, wanted his hands now caressing her firm breasts to touch her even more intimately. Instinctively she knew that this man would be all she'd ever imagined.

After several ecstatic moments, Melissa knew she must pull away from Brandon. She wanted him, wanted him badly, but as his name came as a groan from her throat, a warning flashed through her impassioned nerves. She was kissing Brandon Kade. Abruptly, she pulled her passion-bruised lips from his, knowing she had to stop now . . . or never. Senses reeling, heart pounding wildly, her mind clearing, she realized with a shock this was only the second man who had ever completely aroused her sexual passions.

"Snowbird, darling little Snowbird. I've wanted you since the moment I first saw you," Brandon whispered, holding her straining body tightly, his words burning against her heated cheek. Melissa felt the strong beat of his heart pulsing against her breast as his meaning registered. Perplexed, she renewed her attempt to pull away from him.

"It isn't really me you want," she accused. Great hurt mingled with sudden fear that she was just another in his long string of conquests. "You don't even *know* me," was her breathless indictment. Slowly she watched his eyes harden, taking on the hooded, guarded look of a magnificent falcon.

"You're wrong there. I know enough about you already to want you, Snowbird, but not until you want me too. And you will, I promise you that."

Ludicrously, the electronic alarm on Brandon's watch beeped clamorously, breaking the tense, emotion-filled moment between them—irredeemably shattering the mood of passion that held them. Reluctantly he released her with a sigh of resignation.

"I'm sorry to say I have a flight to make, or we might have brought this matter to a far more satisfactory resolution," he said regretfully as he opened the door, allowing the chill night air to rush into the interior of the car.

At her door he bent so low, so close, she was afraid he'd hear the erratic beat of her heart. His breath seemed to caress her lips. "Good night, Snowbird. See you in La Jolla."

Senselessly, Melissa felt a sharp twinge of disappointment when he failed to kiss her again before walking away.

CHAPTER FOUR

Alone in her eclectically furnished apartment, Melissa couldn't get thoughts of Brandon Kade out of her mind. It was as though the touch of his lips had flipped a switch in her emotional fuse box, completing a circuit that had shorted out long ago. A real turn-on, she laughed wryly, kicking off high-heeled pumps to wiggle rainsoaked toes. I'd better get out of these wet clothes before I electrocute myself with all this supercharged energy, she flippantly told herself in an effort to diminish the flaming impact of his assault. Instinct warned she was playing with fire. Her nerves jangled unendurably.

Walking to the corner window of the third-story suite, she gazed out to where fog and steady drizzle indistinctly blurred Seattle's landmarks to flat, dark silhouettes against the muted glow of the night city sky. She tried vainly to shake off the tingling excited feeling of unease his touch had triggered. Although attracted to the vibrant coiled power of his muscular body and held by his keen wit and piercing intellectual brilliance, she was nevertheless repelled by cold reality: he was from one world and she from quite another. Soon Brandon Kade would be flying south, back to his main offices and home in San Francisco. Would he give her more than a passing thought? Doubtful, very doubtful.

But his words "See you in La Jolla" held a promise, didn't they? No, she was reading too much into that passing remark. Chances were he wouldn't even recognize her at Julia's wedding—by then her face would be replaced in his memory by that of a dozen or more women far lovelier than she. She had to forget him, but the harder she tried, the more clearly she pictured every appealing line and angle of his face and body.

To avoid having to discuss the evening when Julia returned, Melissa firmly closed the bedroom door. Her experiences were too fresh, too vivid, too confusing to share. Perhaps by morning she'd have sorted out her tumultuous feelings and have gained control of her emotions.

Besides, with graduation so close and the grueling tedium of studying for her bars still to come, Melissa reminded herself sternly, she had more important things to think about than a man she barely knew. As the water splashed noisily into the tub, she determinedly turned her thoughts to the past three years. Diffused glow from the streetlight spilled into the starkly white tiled room from a large recessed opaque window, creating oddly interesting patterns where the deep green foliage of an ivy plant blocked its entry. She remembered how the profusely growing grape ivy had been a single leafy strand in a little pot she'd hopefully placed on the windowsill when she and Julia had first decided to take the apartment together.

Jana had grown like that ivy, grown more quickly than Melissa had ever thought possible. It had been painfully difficult to leave her daughter in Alaska while she'd pursued her law degree—if only she could have witnessed every stage of Jana's development as she had the plant's. Without question Jana had been well cared for and loved by her grandfather and Irene Turner, the housekeeper. But Melissa would never forget the agony she'd felt each time Jana had greeted her at the airport in Anchorage—noting how the child had grown, how she'd changed since they'd last been together.

Many times during these long months her resolve had weakened and she could have easily thrown all thoughts of a law degree out the window. But reason and purpose had returned each time she'd seen Jana's hand clasped firmly in Laurence Bennett's, as if he expected his granddaughter to take the place of his lost son—as if he expected Jana and Melissa to fill the void in his personal life. Stumbling blocks loomed large on the road to a happy future, but Melissa was determined to overcome them one by one. Establishing a serious career of her own was the first and most important step in becoming independent of her father-in-law's loving domination.

After testing the temperature of the water with her fingertips, she dropped her terry robe and lowered her slim body into the delicious warmth of the frothy water. Leaning back, her nervous tension dissipating, she rested her head on a bath pillow, once again allowing herself to dwell a little more objectively on the evening's events. Julia had been right—it hadn't been dull. Brandon Kade was as flamboyant and attractive as the media made him out.

Lazily turning her toes in a slow circular pattern, flexing and then relaxing the muscles of her shapely calves and slender ankles, Melissa considered the assumptions she'd made about the man before actually meeting him. She'd just assumed he took on sensationally controversial cases solely for the publicity. But after listening to his speech and hearing the surprising disclosures he'd made to her, she no longer believed that to be so. The challenge those cases presented was probably an important factor in his decision, she suspected, and of course money and prestige were obvious considerations. Still, somehow, she knew that the opportunity to use his uncanny legal skill had to be the major part of his satisfaction: he was a man who liked to win.

But there was even more to it than that—there was a goodness in him she'd never suspected. Rarely given to fantasizing, to her surprise she found herself imagining Brandon mounted on a glorious white steed, an armored knight of the legendary round table, fulfilling his vow of "might for right" as he battled for justice in the courtroom.

What frivolous nonsense! Melissa told herself, lifting a mound of bubbles on the back of her slim hand, then gently blowing them toward the ceiling. She wished her memories of the black-haired, light-eyed man and the tightly bridled feelings he'd so easily unleashed in her would disperse as easily as the bubbles.

A blast of unseasonably cold wind forced beating rain against the opaque window as Melissa stepped from the tub, causing her to shiver. This unproductive line of thinking had to stop, she decided. She had no room in her life for any man right now. Everything was already far too complicated. It was time to go home: a new career awaited her, she had to meet her obligations to her father-in-law, and most importantly, she had to become Jana's full-time mother. Try as she might, there was no way she could picture the impressive attorney with a small child, and there was no way she could risk becoming involved with a man who couldn't easily assume the role of father to her fatherless daughter. A man who believed in loyalty to himself first was *not* for her, no matter *how* intellectually stimulating and physically attractive he might be.

Still, as Melissa snuggled under the rose down quilt of her solitary bed, she knew the embers of her passionate nature which had lain coolly dormant for so long had been fanned to flame once more. Her dreams were disturbing . . . stimulating . . . tormented . . . wildly wonderful . . . deceptively treacherous. Her restless body remembered his touch, his taste, his feel. Brandon's drawling husky words—"Do you have any idea how beautiful you are, Snowbird?"—were repeated over and over in her mind, alternating with his dismissingly mocking ones: "because you are a woman."

It was a beautiful night for flying, Brandon realized, a few miles south of Seattle, pulling the small corporate jet owned by his firm out of the low-hanging rainclouds covering the City on the Sound. The air was crystal clear, the black sky full of sparkling stars. As they flew down the western coastline over jewel-lit cities, Brandon knew that he and his young associate, Scott, were both thinking about the women they'd left behind. Brandon was particularly glad on this night to be piloting the powerful plane. Some considered the sleek aircraft to be simply a carefully calculated part of his flamboyant image, he well knew, but their assumptions were off base. Without the freedom and mobility it provided, he'd be unable to handle the cases he took on with such success. Additionally, he thought with an ironic grin, his critics overlooked one of the jet's most important assets: it served as an unsurpassable tax write-off. At the moment he had it perfectly under his control, and tonight he needed to feel in control of something, he admitted ruefully—his feelings were getting out of hand.

For much of the flight Brandon was engrossed in thought. Suspecting Scott's silence was partly due to an assumption that his boss was concentrating on the case, Brandon knew the young attorney couldn't be more wrong. The face and form of the petite blonde, Melissa Collins Bennett, were all his mind's eye could see.

Reliving the moments he and Melissa had shared in the darkened car, he'd been unprepared for the soft vulnerable innocence he'd found in her warm, eager, but surprisingly inexperienced embrace. After all, she was a widow with a small child! But his mouth had never touched softly trusting lips like hers. His arms had never held such fresh pliant sweetness. Once kissing her, he'd found himself immediately aroused, almost unable to stop. He'd been surprised to find that her cool, fragile, porcelain-skinned exterior enclosed such a warm passionate nature. Astounded, he simply couldn't believe the effect she had on him. Her guileless simplicity was something he'd never encountered in his considerable experience. It was fortunate she'd broken away from their compelling, consuming embrace or he might have alarmed her with an unexpected, unpremeditated display of passion. The longer he pictured her fine-boned face, his memory tracing the outline of each delicate feature, the more exquisitely beautiful he realized Melissa was. It would take a connoisseur to fully appreciate the classical qualities her face and form embodied.

Having thought himself jaded and completely disillusioned by encounters with women, his disastrous marriage and subsequent divorce had left him empty of any desire for emotional entanglement. To be honest, with Felicia he'd known from the start that the sensual need they'd shared had had little, if anything, to do with genuine caring. The ending of their marriage had wounded his pride, not his heart. But Melissa was different. She needed to be taken care of—to be protected and cherished. Never having experienced this feeling for a woman before, he wondered: could this possibly be love? Emotionally numb since the divorce, he felt as if just being with Melissa had pumped revitalizing blood through his veins.

Touching her slight body, holding her softly yielding flesh in his arms, had caused a rebirth of feeling, a sharpening of dulled senses that he'd thought impossible.

How does one proceed with a love affair with a girl like that? he asked himself. He'd never felt more sophomoric. Quite an accurate assessment, he realized, with silent humor. Perhaps it was ridiculous, but he felt as if he'd just escorted the campus queen home from the senior prom and been rewarded with her first kiss. Could this woman with her cachet of sophistication and charm be as genuine and artless as she seemed?

Until tonight he'd thought he didn't want another commitment to any woman, and he knew for certain that with this girl any real involvement could lead *only* to marriage. A marriage that would be totally unlike the meaningless charade he'd played out with Felicia. Almost dreamily, he imagined sharing a home with Melissa. She would not only be there to greet him each night, she would be there for *him:*

her blond head on the pillow beside him, her soft womanly body cradled against his heart—there, to offer the solace and loving comfort he'd never had.

Melissa curled her legs up comfortably in the wide velour seat. Beside her Jana sat contentedly, her headset plugged into the airliner's sound system, enjoying the movie that flickered wordlessly on the cabin screen. Melissa had spent the weeks since graduation busily packing up, having her car and furniture loaded onto a barge bound for Anchorage. Days shared with her daughter had been delightful, but nights had been vaguely, namelessly lonely. As the hours of sleepless darkness deepened around her, visions of Brandon Kade's remarkable face had invaded her thoughts along with the memory of his sensuous caresses. Unhappily, her fascination with the famous attorney had not subsided.

Perhaps seeing him in California on a daily yet informal basis would dull his luster . . . allow her to learn to take him for granted as Julia so easily did. Perhaps that would lay this hopeless infatuation to rest.

The heat of the San Diego summer hit them like a blast furnace when they left the terminal, hurrying to the welcome air-conditioning of Julia's waiting car. Her smiling face had been there to greet them when they'd stepped from the ramp, and as they drove through the city and on out the ocean highway toward La Jolla, she kept up a steady stream of conversation.

"Did those tapes you ordered through the Alaska Bar Association ever arrive?"

"Yes, finally. I was afraid I'd have to go up there and get them. Fortunately someone called from the dean's office—the day before our phone was turned off—to tell me they'd been shipped to the school."

"I'm certainly glad you didn't let studying for the bar keep you from coming. And we *will* leave you alone for as much time as you need."

"Thanks. I really appreciate your generosity. Do you realize there are fifty tapes and five volumes on law in general and ten more tapes for the Alaska portion? It seems overwhelming."

"I know it, and I'm already dreading *my* exams even though they're several months down the road. You've been such a great student I'm sure you'll pass the bar with flying colors."

"I'm not so sure about that," Melissa muttered. "I may have to resort to using earphones and running this stuff in my sleep!"

"That's a great idea," Julia responded with wry sarcasm. "But only if you plan to *take* your bars in your sleep! You'll manage. Maybe being around my dad and Brandon you can pick up a little through osmosis—though I can't say it ever worked for me. But I'm glad I didn't set my wedding date until the middle of August: you'll have the whole ordeal behind you by then.

"I'm glad you're here, Jana," Julia said, turning to the little girl. "Now we can get your dress made to fit. You're going to be such a beautiful little flower girl, no one will even notice *me*." Julia pouted with mock petulance.

"You mean I'm going to have a wedding gown?" Jana asked, her eyes widening.

Julia chuckled. "Yes, you are, sweetie. It'll be long and white, trimmed with a deep rose ribbon."

"Can I throw my flowers up in the air?"

"You can throw your rose petals anywhere you'd like." Julia smiled indulgently. "But in the meantime, while your mother's busy studying, there'll be lots of things for you to do. You can swim, play tennis, sail . . ."

"But I don't know how to sail or play tennis, Aunt Julia," Jana protested in her sweet high voice.

"Don't worry about that, honey," Julia assured her. "There'll be plenty of people anxious to teach you. We're going to have so much fun!"

"Do you have any children to play with me?" Jana asked hopefully.

"Not yet, dear," Julia laughed. "But you'll have Aunt Grace and Uncle Warren, who are my mother and father—and Uncle Scott and Uncle Brandon will often be here. And I'll invite some of my friends' children over to play with you too."

"Who's Uncle Brandon?" Jana asked, picking up on the only name she didn't recognize.

Melissa looked sharply toward Julia. Uncle Brandon? she wondered. Those two words hardly fit together in her mind.

"He's a friend. He's almost like a brother to me," Julia explained.

"Is Brandon here?" Melissa couldn't keep herself from voicing the question she'd wanted to ask the moment she'd stepped from the plane.

"He will be in a week or so. He and my father are out there somewhere." Julia gestured toward the incredibly blue sea stretching out to the horizon beyond low sandy dunes. A few gnarled windswept trees were the only visible vegetation. "The last time they radioed in, Brandon asked specifically if you'd arrived." There was a note of curiosity in Julia's voice as she glanced at Melissa appraisingly. With a little more than passing interest, she added, "Is there more going on here than I know about?"

"I'll talk to you later." Melissa nodded meaningfully in Jana's direction. Brandon had asked about her? A pulse began throbbing at her temple.

Julia pointedly changed the subject. "Prepare yourselves," she warned facetiously. "As soon as my dad arrives back you'll be on candid camera. He's turned into a camera bug."

"A camera bug?" Jana asked.

"Yes, the kind of bug that jumps out and snaps your picture whenever you're not looking! He's caught me in every pose imaginable. So be ready for him!"

With that Julia turned her Mercedes sedan into a lane

lined with tall waving palms and stopped the car outside a high stucco wall. She tolerantly let Jana struggle up between them to push a button on the instrument panel which opened massive black wrought-iron gates. Driving up the long circular drive she stopped in front of a large, sprawling terra-cotta roofed mansion, perched on a promontory overlooking the Pacific Ocean.

Looking around admiringly at the Spanish-style home with its many balconies dripping lavish flower-laden vines, Melissa recalled that not only had Julia's father been a senior partner in a prestigious eastern-based law firm before becoming a municipal, then a federal, judge, but that her mother was an heir to a large petroleum fortune. This accounted for the extreme opulence of the surroundings, but Melissa was still unprepared for the grandeur of the estate. Julia's lack of unpretentiousness made it difficult to reconcile this display of wealth with her democratic attitude toward life.

From the moment a smiling Hispanic servant opened the doors to the impressive entryway, life became idyllic. Half expecting a somewhat dark, formal interior, Melissa was pleasantly surprised by the vast inner courtyard filled with natural light and planted with shrubs and flowers.

Accompanied by a small white dancing poodle, Julia's mother came to them quickly across the ceramic tiled floor, extending both her hands in welcome. "Melissa. Jana. We're so glad you could come at last," she said with a smile.

"Thank you, Mrs. Raymond. It was kind of you to have us," Melissa responded as Jana dropped to her knees to embrace the playful wriggling dog.

"Not at all, dear, but you must remember to call me Grace. And this is Tootsie." The petite silver-haired woman indicated the prancing poodle. "We'll show you to your rooms and give you time to freshen up before lunch," she added, walking them toward the spiraling wrought-iron staircase.

She left them to themselves in a second-floor suite, furnished with the finest Iberian antiques. Melissa drew aside louvered doors onto a wide balcony that opened out to the surging Pacific.

Jana looked a bit concerned. "Mommy?" she started.

"What, honey?" Melissa asked, fearing her daughter was already feeling homesick for Alaska.

"It's nice here, but the waves make so much noise, do you think we'll ever get to sleep?"

"I'm sure we'll become used to it very quickly, dear. Some people say the sound of the ocean is like a lullaby."

She hugged her little daughter close, her mind flying out over the water willing Brandon Kade to know she'd arrived . . . willing him to come to her, yet dreading the actual moment they'd meet. In her dreams and thoughts of the past few weeks she'd clung to the memory of being cherished . . . wanted . . . by a strong man. She really didn't want that wonderful feeling to die, to shrivel on the vine before it could burst into bloom. Perhaps it would have been better if she'd never seen Brandon Kade again. Perhaps then her fantasies could have remained intact, rather than dwindling away in the rejection and disappointment she feared. Mother and daughter stood quietly on the balcony enjoying the warmth of the southern sun as a slight breeze ruffled their hair.

"You didn't level with me," Julia accused, perching on the side of Melissa's bed after Jana had fallen asleep that night.

"What are you talking about?" Sitting on the far side, Melissa played innocent, continuing to brush her glossy hair.

"You know what I'm talking about: you and Brandon. What happened between the two of you that night in Seattle?"

"I told you what happened. I became furious with him and walked out of the restaurant like an idiot, and he followed me, rescuing me from a drunken vagrant."

"That's all?" Julia persisted.

"What else could there be?" Melissa evaded coolly.

"A great deal." Julia leaned forward to rest her weight on an outstretched palm. "Although Brandon tried to sound casual when he asked about you, he didn't manage to pull it off. Even my mother has been asking questions."

"I can't imagine what else I could tell you." Melissa's heart thudded.

"Well, I can. There's one thing I've always wanted to know about Brandon."

"I'm sure you know far more about him than I'll ever know."

"Not about this."

"About what?" Melissa asked uneasily, looking away from the probing scrutiny of her friend's gaze.

"Is he a good kisser?"

Snatching up the first thing she could find, Melissa threw a soft, ruffled pillow, which Julia effectively ducked. "How would I know?"

"You know," Julia answered sagely. "You might be able to keep your tone even, but you haven't been under the California sun long enough to account for a face as red as yours is right now. Your beet-red complexion is a dead giveaway."

Melissa exploded, slapping the hairbrush on the bed. "Damn it! It's a good thing I'm going into corporate law. The way I blush is hardly an asset for a trial lawyer."

"As long as you were telling the truth and your own emotions weren't involved, I'm sure you'd do fine," Julia said placatingly. "I'm sorry I teased you. I think it's great if you two've got something going. Brandon deserves better than he's ever had. You'll be good for him."

"What are you *talking* about: I'll 'be good for him'! I barely know him," Melissa protested strenuously, unappeased.

"True love can strike like lightning," Julia proclaimed grandly.

"Maybe so," Melissa agreed, "but its results can be and often are just as disastrous."

"Then you admit it! The two of you *are* in love! I knew it! I have a sense for those things. What could be better, Brandon and my best . . ."

"Don't be ridiculous!" Melissa felt her voice rise, then lowered it so as not to awaken Jana. "You're making a mountain out of a molehill."

"But he did kiss you." Julia's eyes narrowed. "You will admit that."

"Yes," Melissa sighed. "He did kiss me."

"How was it?" Julia pressed, her eyes twinkling.

"Julia! We're twenty-five and twenty-eight—not fifteen and eighteen, for heaven's sake! That's something you'll *never* find out." Melissa smiled mischievously, hugging her knees to her chest.

"I've found out enough to make me very happy," Julia replied smugly.

"Julia, you're making far too much of this. There's no chance of anything serious ever developing between Brandon and me."

"I'm not so sure of that, and I'm not sure you are either," Julia countered perceptively. "After Felicia, you're just what the doctor ordered. Now *that* was a bitter pill for him to swallow."

"What actually happened there?" Melissa couldn't resist asking.

"That devious little schemer went after Brandon with a vengeance, and when she got him, she used him as a stepping stone to fame and fortune. All she wanted was his money and to get inside the doors his name would open. Few people know this"—her voice lowered confidentially—"but Brandon read about their impending Mexican divorce in the morning paper. She hadn't even told him of her plans! She ran off with a sleazy producer who promised to star her in his next film. I understand it completely bombed.

"She was never right for him. They had absolutely nothing in common—outside of bed, and even then their careers kept them apart most of the time. It was amazing, though, how she managed to show up at the end of every case, so she'd be hanging on his arm whenever the photojournalists were on hand." Julia shook her head in disgust.

"My mother won't admit it, but I know she just detested Felicia. Whenever that little hustler didn't have anything better to do, she'd come down here and move in, ordering the servants around, entertaining her loud guests around our pool, acting like she owned the place! We never told Brandon, because we didn't want to hurt him.

"But you"—she turned her attention to Melissa, who straightened up self-consciously—"you're just the woman he needs. My dad thinks Brandon has a promising future in politics if he ever decides to throw his hat in the ring. But for that he needs the right woman beside him. You're the right woman, Melissa; I just know you are!"

"Julia, first of all there's nothing between Brandon and me. I will admit I was starry-eyed meeting such a famous man, but that's all there was to it," she lied, trying to control the blaze that flamed anew in her cheeks. "And much more importantly, I'm not interested in being the 'right woman' for any man. Have you forgotten all our hopes and plans for our own careers? Do you want to be thought of as the 'right woman' for Scott?"

"Yes, I most certainly do, and I want him to be thought of as the right man for me! That doesn't mean that either of us will ever be subservient to the other! Scott and I have already discussed this issue thoroughly, and we both know where we stand. I'll have my career *and* my man."

Melissa sighed deeply. "That may be possible with some men, and Scott is one of them, I'm sure. But Brandon Kade is another matter altogether. He doesn't even want women in the law profession, as you very well know. Are any of his partners women?" Melissa knew that she and Julia were only too aware of the answer to that.

"Not yet," Julia admitted, "but remember, I intend to be the first."

"I'm sure you will be if anyone is." Melissa rose. "At times I wish my future were as clearly laid out as yours. I'm not sure what lies ahead, but one thing I know for certain is that my humble plans won't include the illustrious Mr. Kade. And right now, my dear friend, I've got to get to bed. Tomorrow I have to start wading through that impossible pile of tapes and books!"

Within a few days they'd settled into a comfortable routine. Julia and Grace entertained Jana while Melissa spent many hours each day studying for the bar. For the first few days Jana was delighted having her own private pool in the sun, so Melissa spent what free time she could there, enjoying her little daughter. They were both fond of the water and soon became tanned all over.

One day as she and Jana were trying to outdo each other with crazy silly dives off the diving board, Melissa surfaced to the sound of clapping and a deep masculine voice saying "Bravo!" Recognizing the voice's owner immediately, her heart flipped crazily and a shock wave rocked her body. Gasping, she sucked in some of the water streaming down her face and coughed spasmodically. Horrified, she realized that Brandon Kade had witnessed her jump-up, double-twist, bottom-first splash into the pool. The pink string bikini she wore had been fine a minute before, but suddenly it seemed entirely too skimpy. Confronted by his bold gaze, she realized the bikini left very little of her anatomy to his imagination.

This was not the way she'd planned their meeting. She'd envisioned at least being fully clothed, her makeup carefully in place, and her hair blown dry, not plastered wetly to her skull. She wanted the water to swallow her up. But instead, she watched fascinated as he shed his swim jacket, revealing broad tanned shoulders and a muscular chest thickly covered with springy black hair that tapered down to a narrow line over his flat abdomen and disappeared intriguingly into low-slung, snug-fitting trunks. As if enjoying her attention he slowly took a mouthful from the glass he had placed on the table and with long, strong, well-proportioned legs strode surefootedly to the diving board.

Melissa and Jana floated on their backs as they watched him confidently mount the board. With two energetic bounds on the end, he sprang into the air in a mock swan dive, arms outspread, splashing down in a belly flop. Then his sleek figure was gliding under water, swiftly closing the distance between them like a well-aimed torpedo that threatened to explode Melissa's tenuous composure.

"How was that one?" he asked, surfacing so close that she could see fine traces of silver glistening at his temples and the laughter lighting his slate-blue eyes. "As good as your mother's?"

Jana smiled shyly in reply.

"Hello, Melissa," he drawled, giving her name the unique inflection she remembered so well. "Here we are in La Jolla." Melissa's heart raced, remembering the promise he'd deliberately left unspoken.

"Hello, Brandon," she managed evenly, though her senses hadn't recovered from the bombardment of the sight of his near-naked body. "This is my daughter, Jana."

"You'd never have to tell me who she is," he said with a smile. "She's a tiny replica of her beautiful mother." Melissa was grateful for the bouyant water supporting her; had she been standing during this exchange her traitorous knees would have unquestionably given way.

"I've been watching you from my room, and though I could hardly tear my eyes away, I couldn't wait to get out here and show you some real 'flinging.' We used to do it in college. I'd forgotten all about it until I saw you in action.

You're both very good at it, but perhaps I can show you a new twist or two."

"Jana's been teaching me new things all afternoon." Melissa struggled to remain coherent, disturbed by his exciting nearness.

"You mean this little duckling?" Without warning he scooped Jana from the water, seated her yellow-suited little body on his broad palm and, biceps bulging, flung her into the air with the athletic ease of a professional quarterback. Hitting the water with a resounding splash, the child came up laughing and begging for another lift. Tirelessly, Brandon flung her into the pool time after time. Their friendship was spontaneous, immediate.

Melissa used this completely unexpected distraction to swim to the edge of the pool, pulling herself up onto the tile rim. She hadn't been able to picture him with a child? How wrong she'd been on that score! Perched there with her slender legs dangling in the water, her heart visibly pulsed in her breast. Time hadn't dulled in the slightest the impact he made on her reeling senses, on her vulnerable heart. Had she honestly thought that it would? she asked herself critically. Smoldering obsession burst into flame, as she slowly took in his nearly naked form, inch by glorious inch. Sparkling water glistened like diamonds on the rippling muscles of his strong tanned back. Golden radiant sunlight glinted in his laughing eyes, emphasizing his strong white teeth. He looked young, much younger than she remembered, as he frolicked with the happy child.

Swimming to the far side of the pool, he carried Jana to the diving board, seating her squarely on his broad shoulders. Pausing, he slowly examined Melissa's body, his provocative gaze bringing with it an acute awareness that she was as exposed as he was. His ardor-filled eyes lingered hungrily on her breasts, caressed her abdomen, explored her legs, causing her to quiver.

"Come on, come on!" Jana shrieked impatiently from her

perch atop his neck, flaying tiny heels against his chest, intolerant of the delay.

In response, the set of his eyes changed immediately, regaining the look of pure pleasure. Securely holding Jana's little legs, her childishly round arms wrapped tightly around his forehead, his gaze never leaving Melissa, Brandon jumped into the pool, creating a colossal splash. Jana surfaced immediately and looked around for Brandon, who was nowhere to be seen.

Without warning, his head suddenly popped up directly in front of Melissa. Smoky blue eyes impaled her. "Come back into the water, Snowbird," he called, his velvet voice drawing her into an exclusively adult intimacy. He was no longer boyishly playful; his eyes clearly told her the game he had in mind was not for children. A warm current of desire weakened her resistance.

Intense excitement shot through her, tingling every nerve path into absolute awareness as large-boned fingers encircled her slim ankles, striking her with the immediacy of his maleness. Strong hands grasped her shapely legs, relentlessly sliding her body down the length of his. His powerful hands radiated passion as they moved over her rounded buttocks to the hollow of her spine, holding her to the hardness of his thighs for a brief electric moment. Trying to deny a spurt of consuming desire sparked by this act, she raised her hands to his square shoulders and pushed herself away.

Out of nowhere, a small compact body hurled itself onto Brandon's neck. Caught off guard, he sank under the sudden impact of the gleeful child. Spluttering, gasping for air, he rose to the surface, his head still tightly clutched in the childish embrace of Melissa's determined little daughter.

"Let's jump in again, Uncle Brandon. That's a lot of fun!"

The brief moment of passion had been effectively squelched by this innocent source. Melissa's peals of laughter were joined by Brandon's deep resonant chuckle as he playfully flicked a splash of water in her face.

Their hilarity had not gone unnoticed by the rest of the household. During the afternoon the pool area rang with laughter as they abandoned themselves to silliness of all sorts. A darkly tanned Julia blithely donned her bikini and joined them, while Warren and Grace sat by the pool encouraging their antics. Tootsie cavorted at the edge, running from end to end, barking with excitement at all the commotion. His camera always at hand, Warren grasped the opportunity to take a number of action shots of the prominent attorney engaged in riotously funny play with the two beautiful young women and the adorable child.

Later that afternoon, while she and Jana were lying down in their shuttered, hushed suite for a rest before dinner, Jana exclaimed, "Oh, Mommy, I never had such a good time! Wasn't it fun?"

"Yes, dear. It was great fun."

"Do you think we can do it again?"

"We'll see, honey." Melissa nestled close to her little daughter. Her heart went out to her. Although Jana had been well cared for by her grandfather and the middle-aged Mrs. Turner, she could see the child had missed the pleasure of growing up in a young family. Sonny would have been a playful companion to the daughter he'd never known. His boyish face, the face that had never reached true maturity, rose in her mind.

Sleepily, Jana's sweet voice interrupted her mother's poignant reverie. "Mommy, I love Uncle Brandon, don't you?"

Evasively Melissa answered her daughter with a kiss.

"Do you think he'll play with me again tomorrow?"

Troubled, unable to promise Jana anything where Brandon was concerned—worried that the wonderful day they'd enjoyed might have been all of that sort of thing he'd ever want to indulge in—wanting to shield the little girl from disappointment, Melissa racked her brain for an enticing substitution. "Tell you what"—she brushed wispy bangs from the child's forehead, sweeping her lips across the soft exposed skin—"tomorrow I'll forget all about having to study and take you to Disneyland! How would you like that?"

"Do you really mean it, Mommy?" Jana squealed gleefully.

"Yes, honey, I really mean it."

"I can't wait."

CHAPTER FIVE

"Are we going to settle for more flinging tomorrow, or do you want to start tennis lessons?" the handsome attorney asked his pert-faced little dinner partner. "Better yet, I'll give you your first tennis lesson in the morning—anyone who swims as well as you do will probably be able to pick up enough tennis to beat me by noon! Then maybe your mother can join us in the pool later." A simple private look passed between Brandon and Melissa—a subtle look, admitting there was something unsettled, an unchartered area, a question of how their relationship would develop. Melissa trembled slightly, though a faint smile touched her lips.

Jana's face fell. "But you promised we'd go to Disneyland tomorrow!" Looking at her mother in dismay, yet unwilling to give up the chance to be with her newfound friend, a sudden compromise occurred: "Uncle Brandon, why don't you come with us?"

In her enthusiasm she impulsively hugged his arm. She had caught him off guard: his soup-laden spoon, halfway on its journey to his mouth, splashed back into the bowl. Calmly wiping pale green splotches of chilled creamed cucumber soup from his shirtfront with a linen napkin, Brandon looked decidedly uncomfortable. Poker-faced, though amused, Melissa wasn't sure whether he was more concerned about his appearance or about Jana's suggestion.

Finding the idea of Brandon Kade at Disneyland hilarious, Julia jumped right in. "I'm sure your uncle Brandon would *love* to take you to Disneyland, Jana!"

His wryly raised brow silently acknowledged that the vow Julia made in Seattle to get even with him had been kept. She'd seized the perfect opportunity to make him a hero or a Scrooge in Jana's eyes. Disneyland was one of California's attractions he'd never had any use for. Even when a convention had taken him to Anaheim, he'd steered clear of the place, escaping the hordes of stroller-pushing, camera-toting tourists by remaining safely ensconced in his hotel suite.

Jana jumped up excitedly, throwing her arms around Brandon's neck. "Would you? Would you really take us?"

Brandon's handsome features darkened, and he glowered at Julia. Her quick smirk changed easily to a pretended innocence, though her eyes sparkled with mischief as she stifled laughter under a hurriedly raised napkin.

Sighing deeply, he capitulated, answering with forced joviality, "Of course I'll take you to Disneyland, Jana . . . if you're sure there's nothing else you'd rather do"—the attorney in him was unable to resist one last effort at plea bargaining.

Jana determinedly shook her head in reply, her eyes alight with anticipation.

"Are these plans all right with you, Melissa?" he asked. At the moment, he felt he'd do anything if it meant a chance to spend a day with Melissa . . . and surprisingly, he really liked her little kid.

"You *want* to come?" Melissa asked, gazing at him intently. "I'm sure you must have far more important things to do."

"I want to come," he answered affirmatively. Damn it, let Julia gloat! What did he care . . . she'd unwittingly done him a favor.

Using her need to study as an excuse, Melissa took Jana up to bed after the late dinner, leaving the other four to play a few hands of cards. What she really needed was time to collect herself. This day had been a shocker! First the stimulating episode in the pool, and now this totally unexpected agreement to take them to Disneyland. Certainly Julia had goaded him into it, but still, Brandon Kade wasn't a man who couldn't say no. Urbane and smoothly articulate, he'd have been capable of convincing Jana he was doing her a favor by *not* taking her to Disneyland . . . if he'd wanted to. But clearly he hadn't wanted to.

Why? Why was he doing this? Why was he pursuing her? Was she simply providing amusement for him? Melissa sank into an upholstered wing chair, remembering that night in Seattle, remembering his deeply timbered promise . . . or had it been a threat?—the promise that she'd want him. Was he using her love for Jana to see that that happened? He'd be ruthless enough to do just that in certain circumstances, she suspected. But no, remembering the genuine warmth and true interest she'd seen in his eyes as he'd played and interacted with the little girl, she knew with certainty this was not one of them.

One thing had been apparent—he sure as hell hadn't wanted to go to Disneyland. But he was going . . . and she was going with him! Her mind drifted off, waging silent wars, relentlessly exploring his motives. Damn! She sat bolt upright. It was happening just as she'd feared! He was monopolizing her thoughts, as well as her time. How was she ever going to pass the bar with that man under the same roof?

A part of her facetiously wished that some married senator or another would be accused of conspiracy to murder his mistress's other lover, so that the world-renowned Mr. Kade's services would desperately be required elsewhere. . . . Another part of her dreaded the day when she was sure to come down to find his vacation was over and he'd returned to San Francisco. Indecision settled into inertia as she sat in the deepening evening, foolishly contemplating the wallpaper pattern . . . knowing he was downstairs . . .

After a long while, feeling all at once peculiarly drained of emotion and taut as an aerialist's tightrope, Melissa began preparing for bed. Hearing a tap at the door, she shrugged into a lightweight robe, knowing Julia had stopped by for their usual late evening talk.

Julia was bubbling over with enthusiasm. "Aren't you glad you came? Everything's working out so well—even better, and faster, than I hoped." When Melissa ignored her implied meaning, Julia continued unfazed. "My mother and dad are delighted with Jana. They may never let you take her home!

"I've decided to have a baby right away," Julia announced. "I know they'll be pleased about that. Here"—she tossed Melissa her birth control pill compact—"you'll need these a lot more than I do. Besides"—she allowed Melissa no time for comment—"I think it'll be great to start a child care facility for mothers employed by the firm. I'll really be a groundbreaker—Brandon's first woman trial law associate—and his first associate to nurse her baby on the job!"

"You plan to nurse the baby in the Kade and Associates offices?" Melissa hugged a pillow, muffling her rising laughter. "You can't be serious!"

"I am serious." Julia nodded her raven head. "I think women in the professions have to push for their rights if white- and blue-collar women are ever going to achieve theirs."

"You're right, I know." Melissa sobered slightly. "But as noted as the Kade firm is for setting precedents, I doubt *that's* one Mr. Kade has in mind." Again she buried her face in the pillow, unable to stifle peals of laughter.

Julia grinned. "You're right. But he's very fond of my mother, and if we both put pressure on him . . . well, we'll see. I'm not worried. And speaking of Brandon," Julia continued, "I must say, things are really going well between the two of you!"

"There's nothing between us! How many times do I have to tell you that?" Melissa directly confronted her friend's bold gaze; to turn from her eyes would be an enormous mistake, instantly confirming and elaborating on Julia's notions.

"Oh, come on, now. I'm not going to buy that. I've never seen him the way he was in the pool today."

"Obviously he loves children," Melissa commented lig tly.

"Loves children?" Julia snorted. "Ordinarily he can't *stand* them. He looks upon them as a general nuisance. I don't know how many times I've heard him say that he doesn't particularly care to have any of his own."

"Can't stand children?" Melissa repeated. He'd seemed so taken with Jana she would have sworn he'd enjoyed playing with her. Even at the dinner table he'd been charming to the child, hanging on to her every word. Had he been no more than an actor smoothly playing a part, using her innocent daughter as a bit player? Melissa didn't want to believe that was true, but after what Julia had told her there seemed to be no other logical conclusion. Worst suspicions seemingly confirmed, Melissa felt a sinking sensation in the pit of her stomach.

Blithefully unaware of her friend's thoughts, Julia added, "I never thought it would happen, but I suspect he's becoming as crazy about Jana as he is about you."

"He is not crazy about me!" Melissa objected heatedly. But she had to ask, "What makes you think he likes Jana?"

"All evening he and my mother, if you can believe this," Julia confided, "have been carrying on a running conversation about child development. He's asked every question you can imagine about Jana. He seems to think she might be a one-of-a-kind kid.

"He'll be up to his kneecaps in *real* kids tomorrow," Julia chortled. "I'd love to go with you just to see Brandon Kade at Disneyland! I cooked his goose, didn't I?" Gleefully she collapsed on the bed, rocking with laughter.

"Be my guest!" Melissa offered cynically. "You cooked *my* goose too! I'm the one who has to go. If he turns surly, I'm the one who'll be stuck with him." Although her words were sarcastic, Melissa's heart had lightened hearing that Brandon's interest in Jana was genuine, extending beyond her earshot. Somehow that knowledge was vitally important to her.

"I predict"—Julia melodramatically closed her eyes, pressing fingertips against her forehead—"I predict that Brandon will be charming, and that you'll all have the time of your lives. He'll do that, believe me. Even if he trips and falls headfirst down Alice in Wonderland's rabbit hole and has to be dragged out by his heels—no matter *what* happens, no matter *how* he really feels, he'll *never* let me find out.

"So," Julia said, gaining control of her laughter, "prepare yourself a wonderful day. I'll spend the time on the final fitting of my gown and on some last-minute shopping.

"Just think, in a few weeks I'll be a married woman!" she exclaimed from the door. "Scott's flying in tomorrow night to stay a couple of days. I'm glad you and Brandon are so perfect for each other—that way I won't feel like I'm neglecting you whenever he's here."

"How long will Brandon be here?" Melissa asked, knowing full well she shouldn't.

"Don't worry, he'll be here a great deal. He always pops in and out during the summer," Julia said. "And this year," she added meaningfully, "I have a feeling he'll be here as often as he can!"

Melissa raised her eyebrows. "You're so in love that you see romance everywhere you look! Even in the most improbable, impossible, totally out of the question places!"

"Don't be so sure about that." Julia got out before Melissa firmly pushed the door shut behind her.

The next morning Melissa dressed carefully in royal blue polished cotton—pleated pants matched her crisply tailored jacket, which she wore over a brightly striped top; a knit halter was sensibly tucked into her handbag in the event of very warm weather. She dressed Jana in a bright red handkerchief print jumpsuit, topping her blond head with a white straw cowboy hat trimmed with a band of the red fabric.

As the pair came down the stairs to the entryway, Brandon was waiting at the bottom—his slate-blue eyes expressively admiring, rewarding Melissa for the care she'd taken. Conversation was amazingly easy as they ate a quick breakfast chosen from chafing dishes waiting on the table at poolside. Although the clear sunshine of the La Jolla morning was light-years away from the rain-filled Seattle darkness, the peculiar tension that sparked between them was as real now, as dangerously alluring, as it had been since the first moment their eyes had met.

Settling back into the comfortable seat of the Mercedes Brandon had borrowed for the day, anticipating the two-hour drive to Disneyland, Melissa was surprised when Brandon turned south toward San Diego. "Where are we going?" she asked.

"I don't want to make that long drive up there, do you?" He turned in his seat, directing his comment with a wink to Jana. "I thought we'd fly instead. That way we'll be there in a matter of minutes and we'll have more time at the park. My plane is waiting on the strip at the airport."

Delighted, Jana clapped her hands in approval.

Melissa stiffened, stabbed with antagonism. There it was: that undeniable tendency toward grandstanding that was such an integral part of his personality—a part she found difficult to accept. Why hadn't he mentioned flying the night before, or even this morning, instead of waiting until he was in complete control? Such infuriating presumption! There was nothing to be done now, she decided, turning her head to gaze at the passing landscape.

"Is something wrong, Melissa?" Brandon asked quietly.

"Since you've asked," she responded softly, although there was a slight sarcastic edge to her voice, "I usually don't fly in small planes, and I've never allowed Jana to." Leaning close so her daughter would have difficulty overhearing, she added testily, "I wish you'd asked me before you said anything to Jana."

He searched her face intently. "Here, let's have some music," he suggested loudly with forced cheerfulness, his large tanned hand flipping on the tape deck and then quickly adjusting the backseat speakers.

"What's the matter, don't you trust me? My corporate Lear isn't a light craft, and I'm a well-qualified pilot. I have five thousand logged hours and an unlimited license. I've stayed active as a fighter pilot in the air force reserves, though that isn't general knowledge. I'm moderately confident I can get us to Anaheim and back safely." He smiled reassuringly.

Her reaction was unreasonable—and this was certainly not the time or place to discuss the plane crash that had killed Jana's father. Brandon would never take an unnecessary chance like Sonny had, Melissa felt certain. But all that aside—she resented the fact that he would take for granted that whatever he decided would be all right with her.

"I'm not worried about your credentials. We'll fly with you this time. You and I will discuss it later. Right now I don't want to spoil the day for Jana."

Sitting behind her daughter and Brandon on the flight to Anaheim, Melissa watched Brandon execute a perfect takeoff. A professional, thoroughly competent pilot, he handled the sleek jet with skill and expertise. Melissa couldn't help but think that his masculine beauty perfectly complemented his absolute mastery of the powerful machine. The fine lines of his sun-dark face took on a tender expression as he enjoyed Jana's rapt appreciation, patiently explaining the significance of each knob, dial, gauge, switch, and light.

Having an opportunity to observe him freely without the distraction of his piercing gaze or heart-melting drawl—his deep voice and Jana's treble wove together in a pleasing harmonious duet above the background whine of the jet engines—Melissa allowed herself the luxury of dwelling on his intriguing face, lingering upon each feature. She made a concentrated effort to discover just what about him was so utterly, absolutely fascinating. His presumptuous self-assurance was annoying, even downright irritating, but nothing about him smothered, or even diminished, the attraction he held for her.

He exuded an air of youthful vibrancy belying his professional accomplishments. She knew from having seen it in print a number of times that the was thirty-eight. Silver-shot temples only enhanced the ebony of his hair; crinkling laugh lines etched around his eyes only increased his appeal. Age held no threat to his good looks—he was one of those men who would only grow better-looking as time added to his aura of distinction and authority.

The more she dwelled on the attractive man sitting next to her, the more excitedly her pulse raced, stirring within her the feelings his very presence never failed to evoke. Get a hold on yourself, her intellect sternly warned her wayward emotions, you can't spend the rest of the summer eating your heart out simply because Brandon Kade will be around every now and then.

That chiseled face had launched a thousand tabloids; those sensitive hands had intimately caressed dozens of women; those firm sensuous lips had kissed more beauties than he could probably remember. There was no way she'd ever stand out in the crowd of sophisticates vying for his attention.

Suddenly dizzily overwhelmed by the memory of steel-strong arms around her, his probing kisses tapping her deep well of hidden desire—just as suddenly she yearned to have again the force of his parted lips on hers, yearned to feel the white heat of burning desire course through her veins, wanted to experience in his embrace the intimate sublime pleasure her feminine body had been denied for so long. She had never been so primitively, fundamentally affected by a man: the mere sound of his voice, a chance glance from his eyes, a faint whiff of the clean scent of his lean athletic body was enough to leave her starry-eyed and breathless.

She shook her head slightly, bringing herself back to reality. Come off that cloud, baby, cold reality warned. Even if he were attainable, even if your life could accommodate a love right now, the man relentlessly responsible for torturing your straight little spine with those unceasing prickles of pleasure is the same guy whose respect for women goes no further than their potential to be exciting, stimulating bedfellows—the same guy who has the unmitigated nerve to pity the judge because Julia wasn't born a boy! But somehow those thoughts didn't seem so hopelessly damning to Melissa, isolated in the snug plane thousands of feet in the endless sky, knowing she was going to spend an entire day and evening with the only man—regardless of his infuriating, maddening prejudices—the only man she'd met in long, lonely years whom she wanted to literally pick her up and fly her to the moon on wings of passion.

Upon landing they were whisked to the Magic Kingdom in the limousine Brandon had radioed ahead for. Jana was excited beyond words and wanted to see everything right away! Sensing it might be her only chance, she kept her mother and Brandon going until the park closed at midnight, pulling them from one delight to another. In the fantasy world of blooming flowers and clear sparkling water, under the cloudless blue sky, surrounded by storybook settings, Melissa lost all touch with reality. Walking hand in hand with the most prepossessing man she'd seen all day—

this day or any other—she was stricken with a peculiar painless strain of romantic culture shock.

Her old standards, her old staunchly held beliefs no longer applied. In her star-struck eyes, everything the gorgeous hunk of man at her side did or said seemed undeniably right, unquestionably perfect. She'd never felt more comfortable, more secure, more completely natural . . . or more devastatingly sweetly energized being with anyone. Holding Jana's soft hand on one side, and having hers held by Brandon's large enveloping one on the other, nothing mattered: her concerns about the future evaporated, her worries about commitments and exams were wiped away. There was nowhere else she'd rather be, and no others whose company she'd prefer. As they stood in long lines at each attraction, she welcomed his casually supportive arm around her shoulder or at her waist as she idly chatted with him or simply rested her head against the broad expanse of his chest.

"I can't believe this child," Brandon moaned as Jana, now confident in her power over him, dragged him off for a final ride on Space Mountain after they watched the captivating light parade. "Doesn't she ever get tired?" Chuckling, Melissa shook her head. Jana's stamina had been amazing.

"I'll tell you one thing, little girl," Melissa heard him say as they walked onto the escalator hand in hand. "You're lucky your mother and I don't have 'motion sickness, or heart trouble, or weak backs' as the signs say. Although after today I'm not so sure I shouldn't have a checkup." He gave an exaggerated groan, his free hand holding the small of his back in mock pain.

"Oh, Uncle Brandon!" Jana giggled as they disappeared from view.

Melissa stood in the almost deserted amusement park staring into space. A soft smile spread over her lovely face as images of the day ran through her mind, delicious memories she and her daughter would always treasure. Not only had they basked in the California sun, but they had been privileged to enjoy the full radiant force of Brandon Kade's incredible wealth of charm. Suddenly she felt lonely and exposed standing there without him—almost sorry she'd begged off from the last ride. A broad smile of welcome curved her mouth when she saw them coming down the ramp, Jana riding piggyback. Joyfully she ran forward to meet them, placing her hand in the warmth of his.

"Come on, you two," she urged with a smile. "We're going to have to run to catch the last monorail out!"

That Jana had indeed become tired was apparent on the limousine ride from the Disneyland Hotel to the airport. She fell asleep before the vehicle had pulled away from the parking lot. Cradling her softly in one arm, Brandon casually put his other around Melissa.

"I like your kid," he said in the darkness of the car.

"So I've noticed," she smiled. "She likes you too."

Although exhausted, Melissa found it impossible to relax. She was sitting too close to him, their legs touching intimately in the confines of the car. All she could think of was other intimate moments they'd shared . . . how his embrace had awakened a tremulous excitement within her, how his touch had brought her to life.

Tenderness flowed through her as she silently conceded that, for the moment, she wanted nothing more than to take up where they'd left off that foggy night in Seattle. Finally allowing her body to fit against his, she felt his arm draw her closer to his radiating warmth. When his lips brushed her hair, tenderly lingering at her temple, she smiled in delectable contentment. How ridiculous she'd been to worry about his being in La Jolla. Life was fleeting at best. Each moment was meant to be lived, to be savored. Even though in the long run her relationship with Brandon was doomed, she could no longer deny that she was a little in love with him. How foolish to hold back—how foolish to deny herself the exquisite pleasure of the delights he offered.

As Brandon felt the tension leave Melissa's body, he pulled her closer. His lips burned at her temple, and he felt somehow protective of this woman. She's so sweet, he thought, as sweet and almost as innocent as this sleeping child in my arms. What does Melissa know of the world? How could she defend people accused of murder . . . or worse? How could she face the sordid conditions of jails or the frantic beseechments of victims? How could she stand up to the abusive brutal argumentation that was the hallmark of a criminal trial? Could she browbeat a witness, forcing the truth from him? Brandon shifted uncomfortably, unwilling to think of her in those situations. Much as he hated to think of the influence her father-in-law exerted over her life, he was grateful to the man for insisting she stick with corporate law.

But she was a mother: why wasn't that enough? What was the matter with women these days? he wondered. Thinking of his own mother and how worn-out she had become, he knew how she would have welcomed the advantages enjoyed by typical middle-class housewives. Perhaps she would even have had time to love her children, he thought with a pang of something very close to pain.

Brandon inwardly acknowledged a sense of confusion—something very rare indeed. Until he'd met Melissa he'd been in absolute command of himself and his destiny. Having achieved what he'd set out to do on a far greater scale than he'd dreamed, he felt sure of himself and his power to control the circumstances of his life.

Only where women were concerned did things go wrong. His relationship with his mother had never been resolved. His help had come too late, he thought bitterly. She'd died before he'd been able to do much for her. He was estranged from his sister, and when his marriage had ended in public humiliation and disaster, he'd wanted never to be vulnerable to a woman again.

But yesterday, seeing Melissa once more had stirred up a

peculiar restlessness. Here was a woman who seemed to have the power to make him feel his life was incomplete without her. Unlike anyone he'd ever known, the self-possessed, courageously determined little blonde was well on her way to claiming him captive. Far from being the deterrent he'd imagined it might be that night in Seattle, the fact that she had a daughter made Melissa even more appealing. He'd been missing a part of life that he hadn't even suspected existed before the two of them had come splashing into his consciousness. It was becoming difficult for him to imagine a world without them! He'd enjoyed the day in the pool more than any day he could remember. He'd even enjoyed Disneyland, *truly* enjoyed it with them at his side. He wanted this sense of enjoyment to continue . . . but how could he keep it? What could he do?

He vaguely sensed that this petite woman held the key to his happiness. Look at me, he said to himself, sitting here holding a child with one arm, my other around a beautiful, irresistible, desirable woman who claims that loyalty to her father-in-law and an independent career are all-important! A career? What made her so damned determined to have a career? In his uncomfortable feeling of irritable confusion, he took the only course his profession had taught him: examine and cross-examine.

Without preface or intended malice, the thoughts that swirled in his mind tumbled from his lips in the form of a number of intensely personal questions: "What do you want a law career for, anyway? . . . Can't you see your daughter needs you? . . . Isn't a family enough to keep you occupied? Look at Grace. . . . Haven't you observed what a wonderful life she makes for everyone? I've never heard her say she misses a career: wouldn't you like to be like her?"

Stunned by the rapid-fire barrage, one question hitting her right after the other, Melissa had no time to answer. What brought this on? she wondered. Jarred unpleasantly out of her mood of dreamy happiness, angered by the need she felt to justify herself and her life to this man, she sensed a measure of her old antagonism returning.

Pulling away from his encircling arm, she answered bitingly, "I have been a wife. I had no control over my life during my marriage and I was left a widow expecting a child. Left to cope alone. Life is too precious and transient to expose myself to the danger of being left like that again.

"You have a career, and everything went by the wayside until you'd established yourself, didn't it? Why shouldn't I have the chance to do the same?"

In reply, Brandon gestured toward Jana's tiny sleeping form.

"She's the main reason I feel so strongly about this." Tears stung Melissa's eyes. "I've had to be strong . . . for her. Everything I've done, everything I've sacrificed, has been with her best interests in mind. That's something narrow-minded people without a sense of family loyalty couldn't possibly understand."

Overwhelmed by sudden realization of the responsibility and hardship Melissa had experienced, he changed his tack, softening his tone. "Have you left any room for contingencies?"

"What do you mean—contingencies?" she asked, a puzzled frown furrowing her brow.

"Well, what if you don't like being a corporate lawyer? What if you meet someone?"

"Meet someone?" she echoed.

He sighed deeply, uncomfortable at being forced to spell out his meaning. "You're a beautiful woman and you're going to meet a lot of men who will desire you."

She waited, half expecting him to proclaim he was one, but he was silent. She replied, "That hasn't happened yet." She didn't add: because I've always run in the other direction . . . until now. "So I guess I'll just cross that bridge when I come to it."

They rode a few moments in silence, the harsh blue lights

of the airport entry illuminating the darkness of the interior of the limousine.

"Forgive my courtroom manners." Brandon was sincerely apologetic. "I can be abrasive at times, or so I'm told," he admitted wryly. "I came on way too strong, and I didn't mean any of it the way it sounded. I'm sorry, but you're one thing I can't seem to deal with objectively. When I think of you it seems to be on an emotional rather than a rational level." Placing his arm around her shoulders, he drew her back against him.

Although still somewhat troubled, Melissa didn't resist. His admission that his emotions had inspired that unfair attack touched a raw quivering nerve. Truly, they knew so little about each other that she couldn't expect him to understand her motives, her drives . . . and her fears. If there was to be anything at all between them, they would have to talk—they would have to come to know one another.

At the airport Brandon carefully secured Jana's sleeping form in the backseat of the plane before preparing to take off. After receiving clearance and taxiing to the end of the runway, he was advised there would be a ten-minute delay.

Brandon turned toward her. "It seems a great many people are up late tonight." Looking into her beautiful trusting wide eyes, he moved his face toward hers. "I think you've come to that bridge sooner than you thought." His voice was deep, luxuriant velvet.

"What bridge?" she murmured in low tones, determined to make him spell it out.

"The bridge with the man who wants you, waiting on the other side," he whispered. "Will you take the steps to cross over?" his silken voice posed a challenge

"Perhaps. But there's one condition." Desire darkened sapphire eyes.

"What's that?" he asked, clearly entranced by her sensuous bargaining.

"That I be met halfway." The provocative words slipped out meltingly.

"That can be arranged," he answered suavely, moving toward her, desire blazing from the depths of hot steely eyes.

In the grip of longing she accepted his words—though her mind held a part of herself removed, away from his reach. The bridge between their passion-fired bodies would be easy, so very easy to cross . . . but the bridge between his life and hers seemed infinitely long, treacherously narrow—virtually impassable. But the reality of his nearness, the totality of his attraction, swept away all reserve, like a raging river sweeping away all obstacles in its path.

As if caught on the crest of the tumultuously boiling current, Melissa felt her body lifted into his arms. He cradled her against his chest, and a deep tormented moan rose from his throat. His lips hungrily found hers, fiercely commanding, yet tenderly probing the sweet depths of her willing mouth—clinging fervently, hotly, sending a golden wave of sensation through her trembling flesh that threatened to drown her in the dizzyingly swirling whirlpool of his demanding desire.

Her arms clung to his stalwart neck, so like a storm-ravaged log, the only security available in the buffeting tempest of savagely intense aching need. Leaving her lips burning, his mouth blazed an urgent path to her breasts, pushing aside her small halter top, cupping her rose-tipped flesh, licking the tips to hard firm points, before sweetly plundering their rounded crests, sucking them thirstily, wondrously into the warm recesses of his mouth. Waves of ecstasy mounted, throbbing through her, saturating her senses. Violently running her fingers through his hair, Melissa moaned throatily as her body instinctively arched toward his.

His lips reluctantly pulled from hers as the beating of their hearts quieted to a dull if still-rapid thud. A static voice brought them back to reality.

"November Charlie X-Ray cleared for takeoff runway 7 right," the ground controller directed.

Responding smoothly, never missing a beat, Brandon reached for the mike, his warm eyes smiling into hers. "Roger, Tower. This is November Charlie X-Ray cleared for takeoff runway 7 right."

Putting the mike down, he kissed her softly. "It seems we're destined for an interrupted romance. I pick the damnedest times and places to get things going." He grinned. "I could tell them that I'm having engine trouble and needed a few more minutes," he suggested hopefully. "But no, they'd never let us take off then. We'd end up standing around a hangar all night while they checked this crate over. So"—he sighed, brushing her lips once more—"fasten your seatbelt and prepare for takeoff."

What happens next, Melissa wondered as the darkness enveloped them, her heart still pounding violently. Their intimate wordplay and the resulting embrace had raised more questions than it had answered. She was a fool. Did she really think she could have a little fling with this man and walk away unscathed? She'd have to avoid him—have to turn away from the temptation she found almost irresistible. There might still be time left to come out of this with her heart and emotions only singed and seared rather than irrevocably charred. Glancing sideways at Brandon's strong profile, she felt her heart turn painfully in her breast. Regrettably, there was no other answer.

CHAPTER SIX

The flurry of parties, showers, and activities centering around the wedding left little time for Melissa's studies. She found herself up long after the household had settled into sleep, cramming for her exams. It had been easy for her to avoid any real contact with Brandon—she'd always had a ready excuse. But Jana was a willing companion, eager for the tennis lessons he gave her, and for fun-filled dips in the pool. Many times, sitting in lonely solitude on her balcony, a deep unaccustomed aching pain in her breast, Melissa resisted the strong impulse to join them on the red clay court or in the sun-splashed pool.

At first Brandon's somehow hurtful, quizzical glances across the dinner table had disturbed her, but she avoided responding, trying to hide her misery behind a polite smile. Though he appeared baffled by her behavior, he didn't press for an explanation. Although grateful for his sensitivity, she couldn't help but wonder where and how he fit into her life. She knew only one thing for sure: the days he spent on the estate seemed bright and intense and the days he was gone on business seemed empty—time stood still. She couldn't ignore the pain that seized her heart, or the lump that lingered in her throat during the hours she strove to cast him from her mind—hours during which the monotonous tones of the tape deck nearly drove her from the room—hours during which she suffered the dull ache of desire, remembering the ecstasy of his touch.

One morning Brandon was conspicuous by his absence from the poolside breakfast table, although Melissa noticed a place had been set for him.

"Where's Uncle Brandon?" Jana piped up. "He promised he'd take me for a run on the beach this morning."

"Look over there." Julia pointed across the immense emerald green lawn that ended abruptly at the sand dunes.

Brandon's trim figure ran toward them, a large golden dog loping at his side. When Jana jumped up, running to meet them, Brandon ordered the obedient retriever to a halt. Melissa noticed that her little daughter was unfazed by the size of the silky-haired animal, whose head came nearly to the little girl's chin. Jana's trusting arms encircled its neck as she laid her golden head against the dog's.

"This looks like love at first sight," Brandon remarked pleasantly, though his eyes sent Melissa's a private message.

"That's a gorgeous dog, Brandon, I've never seen her before. Where'd she come from?" Julia asked.

"I got her for Jana," he stated matter-of-factly. "She loves Tootsie so much, she told me she'd like a dog of her own—so I bought her one."

"She's *mine?"* Jana squealed at Brandon's affirmative nod.

"Did you know about this?" Julia asked, causing all eyes to turn to Melissa.

"No," she answered distractedly. It *was* love at first sight for the child and the animal, Melissa realized in dismay, as they ran, tumbled, hugged, and wrestled on the lawn. "Do you think it's safe for her to trust an animal that large?"

"Perfectly," Brandon assured her in a casual jesting way, seating himself at the table. "That dog has a pedrigree an arm long, a faultless medical record, a signed and sealed graduation diploma from obedience school, and is free of germs and fleas—just sanitized, straight from the kennel." Though his tone was light, his eyes searched Melissa's for approval. "Oh, and guaranteed housebroken," he ended.

"You should have asked Melissa first!" Julia scolded.

"You can't give an animal to a child without asking her parent."

"I'm not aware of a law against it," he teased.

"Don't be so flip. You're wrong and you know it," Julia retorted.

"Is there any reason why Jana can't have the dog?" Brandon turned his piercing steel gaze toward Melissa. "If there is I can always take her back."

"No, Brandon. I think it's a little late for that," Melissa answered coolly. "It was very kind of you. Thank you. But her breakfast is getting cold. Do you think you can get her back to the table?"

"No problem," Brandon answered, pulling a dog whistle from his shirt pocket and blowing on it. The dog ran to him immediately, Jana in hot pursuit.

"Lay!" Brandon ordered, and the beautiful dog dropped to the pavement. "Stay!" he commanded, as he swung Jana up in his arms and carried her to her place at the table.

The dog remained motionless throughout the meal except for the rolling of her pleading eyes toward the little girl and the thumping of her plumed tail on the concrete. She stayed, a mound of controlled, quivering muscle even though Tootsie barked vigorously at her before being taken up into Grace's lap.

"I have to think of a name for her," Jana said. As they ate, everyone made suggestions but Jana rejected them all.

The meal finished, Brandon and Jana started toward the beach for their morning romp. Melissa stood alone on the lawn watching their departing figures. The smile slowly left her face as Jana's happy peals of laughter blending with Brandon's deep tones receded from her hearing as they ran after the excitedly barking dog.

She turned to go back to the house but was stopped by Jana's pleading call. "Mom, come on! I want you to come and see my dog run and fetch."

Touched by her daughter's desire to include her in the

special moment, Melissa hesitated slightly, then ran to join her where Brandon waited on the sandy path, a broad smile on his face.

"If I'd had any idea I could get results like this," he teased approvingly, "I'd have bought that dog weeks ago." He fell easily into step beside her.

Acutely aware that this was the closest they'd been since the day at Disneyland, Melissa consciously avoided touching or bumping against him as they walked down the narrow trail. She knew she had to watch her step in more ways than one. She had to keep her distance from his powerful attraction.

Brandon had sensed Melissa's reluctance to be alone with him, but during the days he spent at his office in San Francisco, he couldn't get her off his mind. He'd questioned his motives minutely before reaching the conclusion that he wanted her—and that she was worth his time.

He knew he didn't understand her. She'd been a willing partner the times he'd made romantic advances, but ever since that wonderful day in Anaheim, every time he'd come near her, she'd seemed distant, even indifferent. He just couldn't figure her out.

Whenever he'd given up, deciding it was hopeless, deciding not to pursue her any further, and had returned to the city, he'd become obsessed with the thought that she'd be leaving for Anchorage and he might never see her again. She'd be so far away . . . so removed from his life. If he wanted to make her his, time was running out. Almost panicked, he'd hurry back to La Jolla with this fear in mind, only to be met with a very cool Melissa.

But Jana was a different matter altogether. She was openly delighted any time he appeared—smiling, always ready for fun. He'd never paid any attention to young children before, but from the first time he'd held her wriggling, squirming, compact body in the pool and had experienced the pure trust and exuberant joy of her childish personality, he'd been unaccountably intrigued.

How could a child be so delightful? He was amazed at the intellect and cleverness that little blond head held, at the rapidity with which she learned and grasped new concepts, and at the ability of her well-coordinated body to master and perform tasks he had supposed only adults were capable of. He was a willing captive to this little creature, so alive and demanding, and yet at the same time as feminine and demure as her mother.

He glanced at Melissa, suntanned and shapely, walking by his side. He desired her, needed her, wanted her more than any woman he'd ever known. She was driving him crazy!

On the beach when Jana was playing with her new dog, Brandon turned to Melissa. "I hope you're not upset about the dog," he said somewhat contritely. "It never occurred to me that you might have any objections."

"I was irritated that you didn't ask me about it," Melissa conceded. "But it seems to have made Jana so happy, I don't see how I can object. I am concerned, though, about how we'll get such a large dog home to Alaska." Melissa gazed down the beach toward her daughter and the happy bounding animal, its rich coat gleaming in the sunlight.

Brandon followed her glance. When Jana raised her arm to throw a stick, the dog could easily have jumped up and taken it from her hand, but she waited obediently for her little mistress to fling it into the gentle surf.

"I have to agree with you: it is a big dog." He smiled wryly. "I suppose I should have gotten a smaller one. I really intended to get a poodle, like Tootsie," he admitted. "But—well, it's the kind of dog *I've* always wanted. I know how attached Jana is to Tootsie, and I was afraid it would be hard for her to leave the poodle behind."

When he took her hand in his, Melissa looked up into the fathomlessly deep gray-blue eyes that seemed to be boring into hers. With effort, she looked away. When she tried to withdraw her hand, his grip tightened. "I'm beginning to learn how hard it is to leave something you love," he finished.

He continued talking as their steps slowed to a stop. "I always wanted a dog like that when I was a boy," he repeated softly, a tone in his voice she'd never heard before. Melissa looked up at him questioningly. Though he'd made some reference to a background of poverty the night they'd met, she still couldn't imagine him not having everything he wanted.

"But we were too poor to afford any pets, let alone a big dog like that one. I remember I wanted one so badly I pored over the dog books in the town library, looking at the pictures until I finally decided on the one I liked best. I can still see that picture, the golden retriever in perfect point, its hair so silky-looking and clean, devotion shining from its eyes. I guess I got carried away at the kennels when I walked past this one." He'd never revealed to anyone, other than Warren and Grace, anything about his deprived childhood. Suddenly he felt exposed, shorn of his protective veneer.

Brandon couldn't know it, but Melissa saw in his face traces of the yearning little boy he had been. She felt closer to him at this moment than she'd believed was possible. Her fingers tightened around his in a mute gesture of understanding, deeply moved that he had trusted her with this confidence.

Encouraged by the caring look in her eyes, he continued, "We were so poor that every new child that was born in the family just took something necessary away from the rest. There were a lot of us"—he shook his head slowly at the memory—"badly clothed, squabbling, always a little hungry and never quite clean.

"When I first saw Jana, I couldn't believe a child could be fun and looked upon as a luxury—something to give pleasure and enrich one's life rather than drag it down. She's become precious to me, and she's not even mine.

"That day we spent together in Disneyland really did it. It was the last place in the world I'd have chosen to be—as I suspect you well knew"—the look on his face mingled irony and tenderness—"and yet, seeing it through her eyes made it a day I'll never forget. I've never wanted to have a child myself, remembering my own childhood, but now I'm beginning to see I've missed something. That little girl has me twisted around her little finger, and I hope she never finds out the power she has over me." He chuckled, shaking his head in wonderment. "You're a lucky lady to have a kid like that," he said, somewhat embarrassed at having expressed his feelings so candidly. "But tell me, what kind of childhood did you have?"

He smiled down at her, the tone of his voice shifting to a different level, not quite so confidential or intimate. No longer was he the vulnerable young boy lost in memory. Again he became the commanding man in full control of his emotions.

Melissa's smile faded, and a cloud passed over her features. "Well, I never had a dog either. In fact I never even had a real family. I was told my mother was very young and alone—she tried for a while but she couldn't take care of me. I was placed in a series of foster homes because my mother would never consent to my being adopted. Although I don't clearly remember her, I suppose she hoped someday she could come back for me. Finally, when my mother died, my great aunt Margarite in Anchorage learned of my existence and sent for me.

"I was twelve by then and my maiden aunt, though very kind, found it trying to raise a teen-ager. Although I love her for doing it—anything is better than being shuffled from one foster home to another." Her stricken face told him more than her words—how she had felt being alone, having to adjust to first one situation then another. Again her hand began to slip from his, but he held it tightly, not allowing her to withdraw from him—savoring the moments of closeness they shared. "The first time I ever knew what a real family was, the first time I felt like I really belonged, was with Sonny and his dad. They made me feel they needed me as much as I needed them."

"What about your husband? What happened to him?" he asked softly. She turned her face from his, gazing out to sea. "Melissa," he persisted, his hand cupping her chin, turning her face back, "tell me. I want to know. I have to know."

Her face whitened. As if in a daze she spoke tonelessly, unemotionally, as though still hardened by grief. "I was pregnant with Jana and everything looked so wonderful. We had a house, our own seaplane—Sonny was in training to take over the lumber division of his father's company—which meant he had to commute between Anchorage and Juneau a great deal. One Monday he was supposed to fly in to attend an early morning meeting. He was warned that weather conditions were dangerous. I begged him not to go—he could have easily postponed the meeting. But he was young, brash, self-confident—he wouldn't listen. The weather got worse, and he crashed.

"I really hated him for doing that to me . . . and to our unborn child." Her tear-rimmed eyes were darkened with emotion. "It's taken me a long, long time to forgive him, but I can see now that he was a victim of his own immaturity.

"His dad's heart was broken. He's stood by me like a true father. I feel that I'm as much his daughter as Jana is mine. But one thing I've learned from all this is that I can't ever be dependent upon another person. That doesn't mean I'll ever stop loving or caring, but I'll never be so vulnerable again. Now that I have Jana, I can't trust our future to be in anyone else's hands. I have to know that I'd be able to survive on my own."

"Poor little Snowbird," Brandon murmured, pulling her into his arms. "You've been through so much." Brushing across her smooth forehead, his lips descended slowly, thoughtfully, to meet hers in a kiss as intangibly gentle as the sea breeze. She felt an intimacy not only of the flesh but of the soul. Even though they were each aware of the stirrings of passion, this kiss held a tenderness meant to heal aching need. He cradled her gently, rocking her back and forth, as if to protect her from harm.

Wanting to grasp the moment, to make it last as long as possible, Brandon knew he was in danger of losing control of his emotions. He had to have time to convince her of her need for him. He had to convince her that she had no need for independence—that he would always be there to take care of her. Melissa needed him by her side . . . needed his loving protection. But he'd have to take care, move slowly, or his fragile Snowbird might take flight.

He pulled his lips reluctantly from hers, choosing his words carefully. "Melissa, darling, don't worry about the future. Let's share each day as it comes. Let's take more time to get to know one another—to strengthen our bond of understanding. There are many places in San Diego I'd like to take you and Jana." Never a sightseer, Brandon was surprised to hear himself saying, "It's a fun town with its fair share of attractions. Let's make some plans to take in a few of them, okay?" He spoke with an eagerness generated by his sudden insight.

With his insistent eyes upon her, Melissa felt nervous. She had an impulse to run from him, flee from him. "I'm sorry, I . . . I can't. I have a lot of last-minute studying to do. And then I'm leaving Saturday morning for Anchorage—the bar exams are next week."

Melissa felt as though she were being pulled apart by the wills of two powerful men: her father-in-law in Anchorage, exerting his rational claim to her and her child, and Brandon at her side, exerting his irrational claim to her heart. What's wrong with me? she wondered. When Brandon's gone, I listen for the sound of his voice or the fall of his footsteps, hoping he's returned, but when he's here I don't know how to handle that either.

"Well, then, let me help you study," Brandon offered.

Help her study! If he only knew. His very nearness would drive all other thoughts from her mind. No learning would take place if *he* were helping her. "Thank you, but no. I have to make it on my own."

Disappointed, he felt his smile fading from his lips. He lightly took her by the upper arms and turned her toward him in an attempt to physically draw her back into the closeness they had shared.

"Melissa, what is it with you? You're a beautiful, desirable woman, but you don't seem to realize it or enjoy it. Come on, loosen up!"

Looking down at her with a steady incisive stare, he demanded a response from that guarded gaze of hers. The haunting fear he saw there touched his heart. He smiled apologetically into her troubled face with all the magnetic force of his personality.

Almost hypnotized—as though she had no will of her own—she responded instinctively to the force of his insistent appeal. Eyes shimmering, her face slowly moved toward his, her body weak and yielding. The lips that met hers were not gentle but smothering in their needy, demanding mastery. Giving up all resistance in the wave of gripping passion, she swayed toward him. She found herself kissing him as he was kissing her—fully, wildly, insistently. Shivering as his strong hands moved down the length of her back, she abandoned herself to his touch.

"That's better." The words were part of the caress, as his lips moved against hers.

And again she felt his mouth on hers, demanding and getting the response she had given before. How wonderful to feel his strong arms around her, his hard body pressed to hers! How right to allow her soft curves to melt against him! When his lips followed the firm contour of her chin and her long lovely neck, she could barely breathe for the thudding of her heart beneath her ribs.

When at last he released her, continuing to hold her tenderly, it was some time before her eyes could focus in the bright sunlight to find Jana down the beach still romping with her new pet. Melissa knew her relationship with Brandon had entered a new phase, a phase she was not prepared for. At no time in her life had she experienced the power of another person to so totally physically dominate her. They began to walk down the beach toward Jana, Melissa's delicate hand in Brandon's.

Blond hair streaming behind her, Jana came running to meet them, the golden retriever close at her heels. "Uncle Brandon! Uncle Brandon!" she called out breathlessly. "I've decided I'm going to name my dog 'Brandy' after you."

Melissa felt a shiver as she and Brandon exchanged glances, silently acknowledging another tendril entwining their lives.

Melissa left for Anchorage Saturday morning without Jana. The child had refused to go with her when she'd learned she couldn't take Brandy along. Laurence and Irene were disappointed that Jana had stayed in California, and Melissa had a hard time explaining Jana's reasons to them. She realized Laurence had finally accepted it, however, when she overheard him on the phone planning an elaborate heated doghouse and dog run he was having built as a surprise for his little granddaughter.

The exams were grueling, leaving Melissa exhausted and drained. But her certainty that she had done well left her with a calmness she hadn't felt in months. Calls to Jana assured her that the child was happy—she'd made a new friend, and Brandon had been taking them on daily excursions. Calling herself a coward for doing so, Melissa decided to spend the weekend in Anchorage, resting up, regaining her strength, putting off as long as possible the problem she would have to face. The fewer days she spent with Brandon the better—he'd be her escort at many prenuptial functions during the next few days. She was going to have to cross that bridge he'd talked about or burn it—his lavish attentions to Jana in her absence had made it perfectly clear he didn't intend to give up. Boarding the plane for San Diego, Melissa was in a turmoil: what would she do about Brandon Kade?

Three days before the wedding, Scott's parents, the Lowells, were due to arrive. Although they were staying at a local hotel, they were coming to the estate for dinner that evening, and even as she rose, Melissa could hear sounds of busy activity as the lawns were being groomed and trimmed.

As she started out of the house toward the breakfast table, Brandon took Melissa aside. "Let's go out for dinner tonight. I think it would be a good idea to let the Raymonds and the Lowells have the evening to themselves."

She hesitated. She had to face up to her problem sooner or later, and his suggestion was appropriate. "What about Jana?"

"I know she's been wanting to spend the night with the cook's granddaughter, in the caretaker's lodge," he said.

"Maria's granddaughter?"

"Yes, Rosa. Haven't been able to pry them apart ever since Rosa came to visit. I'll tell you, it's been an experience taking those two little live wires sightseeing and to amusement parks. It's been great though," he chuckled. "Although I have wanted a little *adult* female companionship at times."

Melissa laughed, her heart warming to his generosity. "Of course I'll go with you," she agreed, smiling into his eyes, allowing him to drape his arm casually over her shoulder.

"Good morning, you two," Warren called from the table where the rest were already seated near the pool. Scott, as well as Melissa, had flown in the night before.

"Good morning," Brandon replied heartily, politely holding Melissa's chair, then seating himself next to her. "Well, Julia, today's the day you meet the enemy."

"What are you talking about?" Julia looked at him with dismay. They all turned puzzled faces toward him.

"Correct me if I'm wrong, but it's always been my understanding that one usually finds one's in-laws on a differing side in any given matter than oneself," he said coolly, as he helped himself to scrambled eggs and bacon from a chafing dish.

Indignant at his remark, they all began to speak at once, but Warren's voice with its strong note of authority gained the floor.

"Indeed you are wrong, young man!" Brandon's eyes showed amusement at his mentor's choice of words. "That's a popular notion that has little basis in fact. I think it's quite often the case that one enjoys a warm, free relationship with one's in-laws not unlike that with one's own parents. Certainly it can be the case. It all has to do with the attitude of the parties involved." He scowled darkly at Brandon.

"I'm sure we'll get along well with both our families," Scott interjected, reaching for Julia's hand to reassure her.

"I am too," Julia said, smiling back at him. "I don't know why you find it necessary to be so outrageously callous, Brandon. Sometimes I think you play the devil's advocate just to get everyone going! I don't think even you believe what you say at times!"

"You may be right, Julia," he said, calmly reaching for his orange juice and taking a large swallow. "But this is not one of those times. Believe me, I'm quite serious."

"Oh, Brandon, don't say that," said Grace, thoroughly distressed. "I'm concerned enough about this evening without you making it worse." Suddenly aware of what she had said in her future son-in-law's hearing, she became flustered. "Oh, dear, Scott . . . I hope you understand what I meant. . . . I'm looking forward to having your parents! It's just that I do so want to make a good impression and for us to become close friends. . . . But I'm afraid something might go wrong. . . . Oh," she groaned, "how did this all ever happen?" She shook her head, thoroughly bewildered.

"Of course I understand, Grace. Don't think another thing of it." Scott stared daggers at his boss. "Brandon's just trying to have a bit of fun at Julia's and my expense. I'm sure he had no thought of upsetting you."

Realizing the situation was getting a little out of hand, Brandon said smoothly, "He's quite right, Grace. As a matter of fact I plan to take Melissa to Tijuana today"—Melissa looked at him in surprise hearing this announcement—"and we won't return until late . . . far after dinner. And Jana's going to get her wish to spend the night with Rosa. So you'll have an opportunity to have dinner with the Lowells alone—without the pleasure of the company of the Bennett ladies and"—he winked at Grace charmingly—"without the rather dubious pleasure of my own."

"You don't have to do that, Brandon," Grace protested. "I've already planned on all of you being here."

"No." Melissa, who had sat silently during this exchange, decided it was time to speak her mind. "I quite agree, Grace. This will be a good time for me to have a chance to visit Mexico." She smiled at Jana. "I understand you and Rosa went there with Brandon last week."

"Mexico? Is that where Tea-uh-what-ja-ma-call-it is?" Jana asked, suddenly interested in the conversation, which she had ignored until this time.

"Yes, dear, that's where it is," Melissa answered.

"I remember that place. I couldn't understand what anyone was saying, but Rosa talked for me and Brandon let me buy three big big hats called . . . som-be-ros. One for Nana, one for Papa, and one for me. I wanted to get you one, Mommy, but Uncle Brandon said he'd take you to get your own."

"Then you don't mind if I go with him today?"

"Oh, no, I want to stay with Rosa. She has to go home tomorrow."

"Then it's all set," Brandon remarked, a pleased look on his face.

"Yes, it's all set," Melissa echoed, her eyes sparkling. "However, Brandon, I can't let your earlier remarks pass. I think it's important to get off to a good start with your in-laws. You never know what lies ahead, and they can become far more important in your life than you would ever realize. My father-in-law is as dear a person as I know. I can never repay the debt I owe him." Her voice vibrated with feeling. "I wouldn't be the person I am and where I am today, if it weren't for him." She defiantly met Brandon's eyes.

"I'm sure you exaggerate, Melissa," Brandon replied infuriatingly. "Let's change the subject, shall we?" He turned to Warren and Scott and began discussing a recent Supreme Court decision.

Melissa seethed inwardly at his rude dismissal of her feelings and comments. How dare he treat her like that! She would cancel the Tijuana trip if she hadn't already agreed to his public announcement: she didn't want to create any more anxiety for Grace or Julia. Sighing, she pushed her chair back slightly, the food on her plate untouched. She supposed she had to go. It would make it easier for them all this evening. I'll be doing everyone a favor by keeping Brandon out of the way! she thought with a short derisive laugh.

"Is something amusing, dear?" Grace asked hopefully.

"I was just wondering how Brandon will feel if he ever finds himself in the position of father-in-law someday in the future," Melissa said smugly. *"One's* perspective has a way of changing according to the position in which *one* finds *oneself,"* she said, mimicking his drawling speech.

Although he raised an eyebrow, Brandon resolutely ignored her remark, continuing his conversation as though he hadn't heard.

"That's true, dear," Grace patted her hand. "You'll never know how true until you're my age."

CHAPTER SEVEN

Still irritated, Melissa walked out to the car, where Brandon waited. He examined her diagonally striped, vividly colored sundress: backless to the waist, it complemented her deep tan and sun-streaked hair while displaying her full feminine figure.

"You're beautiful. I'm a lucky man," he said admiringly, bending to open the door of the sleek two-seater sports car.

You're not so bad yourself, she thought grudgingly as he walked around the front of the car. Dressed in trimly fitting navy blue slacks and a white open-necked sport shirt, silver-rimmed sunglasses concealing his eyes, Brandon was at his best. His physical perfection provided a source of constant amazement. She'd never seen him disheveled or in any way less than overwhelmingly attractive—overwhelmingly appealing. The sexual qualities of the moment struck her—somehow being shut in by the door he had closed, waiting passively for him to sit close to her, to start the powerful engine—aroused her in a way she would have found impossible to explain. His virility was stunning, causing a delicious tremor to shake her body.

"Are you in an adventuresome mood?" he asked, pulling onto the highway.

"I don't know," Melissa answered warily, increasingly aware of the building sexual tension—seemingly so inevitable each time they came within touching distance. "What do you have in mind?"

He laughed, a bold rich sound. "Well, I know this great hotel that's famous for its room service," he said suggestively. Seeing her attempt at a very stern expression, he continued, "Seriously, I took the little girls on the trolley from San Diego to the border, and then we walked all over Tijuana, but to my mind that's not real adult entertainment. Now that I've got you to myself for a whole day, I thought we could fly down to Mazatlán. Just takes a little over two hours. Would you like to go?"

Mazatlán. The name conjured up warm, exotic possibilities and blotted out any annoyance remaining from the verbal skirmish over breakfast. And he was asking! He wasn't just taking her compliance for granted! Why not? Nothing demanded her attention—the dreaded bars were behind her, and Jana was happily occupied until tomorrow. She was free! She'd be a fool to turn him down.

"Since you've asked so nicely"—Melissa smiled openly, contentedly, with no hint of the guarded restraint she so often affected in his presence—"I'd love to go. But I do need to let the Raymonds know where we'll be. I can't be out of touch, just in case Jana might need me."

"Sure. That's no problem. We'll call them from the plane. I must admit, though, I didn't think you'd be so easily convinced."

"Why not?" she bantered.

"Correct me if I'm wrong," he grinned, "but at breakfast this morning I got the feeling that you were damn mad—at me."

"Oh, really?" Now genuinely amused, she sparred with him. "You're so perceptive, Mr. Kade. And quite right. The only reason I agreed to go with you was to get you out of their hair . . . and Mazatlán is farther than Tijuana, right?"

"Much farther," he agreed, his grin broadening.

"Then that's reason enough for going there. I'm sure you were correct when you said the Raymonds and the Lowells will have a far more pleasant evening alone." Melissa relaxed, enjoying the amiable give and take.

"I had no intention of upsetting Grace like that," Brandon admitted sincerely, taking Melissa's mild barb in a subdued manner. "I've never seen her so touchy and on edge. It's this wedding business. I'll be glad when it's all over."

"This is one of the highlights of Grace's life!" Melissa exclaimed incredulously, turning slightly to face him. "She's undoubtedly been planning it since the day Julia was born."

"Women. I'll never understand them. On the one hand they want to be taken seriously—as men's equals—and yet they immerse themselves in such trivia."

"Trivia! You're the type of man that would label everything that's beautiful, meaningful, and joyous as trivia," she said hotly. "Can't you understand that Grace wants her daughter's wedding day to be perfect . . . a memory to cherish for the rest of their lives?"

"If you say so," Brandon replied blandly. "It just seems to me that they'll both be so tired and strung out before it's over that they won't be able to enjoy what you're so convinced is supposed to be a marvelous day. But I certainly don't want to ruin *our* day arguing about that. Actually I don't ever find arguing productive, except of course when it involves legal matters. Let's have our fun and leave them to theirs. Shall we?" His easy smile held a barely discernible trace of tentativeness.

Melissa wavered, her mind whirling, unsettled by his dry remarks. What was the use of pursuing the subject any further? More upset than she cared to admit, she realized she hadn't influenced his thinking in the slightest. He just couldn't see the female point of view. She sighed. What did it matter? The wedding would soon be over, and she and this maddeningly dogmatic man would go their separate ways.

Looking at him closely, she watched his expression of faint mockery soften to one of tenderness and concern—almost as though he couldn't understand why she found his views distressing! In that moment her heart went out to him as it never had before—he might be wordly-wise, but he had *so* much to learn. Threatened by something he didn't understand, he was covering his emotions with an aggressive attack on those he loved most.

She shook her head slightly, returning his smile with a forgiving one of her own—and in that same moment she knew she had taken her first bold steps across the bridge that stretched between them. "Yes, let's," she agreed. "Let's really enjoy today."

Airborne, Brandon asked, "Have you ever been to Mazatlán?"

"No. I've never even been to Tijuana. Do you fly down often?"

"Yes, quite often. Whenever my tan starts to fade," he joked. "Seriously, concentrating on a case takes so much out of me that I need a place to rest, to regroup my forces so to speak. And you know that hotel I mentioned earlier?"

"Yes," she ventured, noting the devilish gleam in his eyes. "It's in Mazatlán," she finished for him.

"How'd you guess?" he demanded rakishly.

"It wasn't hard," she answered with mild sarcasm. "But you can forget it." She smiled sweetly, though her pulse raced so wildly she feared its vibrations might interfere with the delicate instrumentation on the elaborate panel, sending them into a nose dive.

Deliberately changing the subject, she commented lightly, though somewhat breathlessly, "It must be nice to have the tropical sun so close." She held out one shapely arm, a heavy gold chain bracelet highlighting the golden bronze tone of her skin. "I've never been this tanned in my life. But I'll be as pale as ever a few weeks after I return to Anchorage."

"There are other places to live," Brandon suggested softly, his words implying more than he spoke. "Other places that might have more to offer you."

What *was* he offering? Melissa wondered. A short time in the sun? A glittering affair—perhaps even an interlude as his pampered mistress? No more than an episode that would leave his life whole—and hers in tattered remnants. After a long moment she spoke. "No. There's no other place. At least not for a long while."

"You might change your mind once you go back there. After all, you've been out on your own for quite a while. You may find you really can't go home again."

"Brandon, I've never been away longer than three months at a time. It's still my home, and with Dad there it will stay that way." Her face clouded. Brandon's comments aroused fears and uncertainties she didn't want to admit, didn't want to recognize. She had to put them aside. Couldn't he see what he was doing to her by acting as though she had a choice? Didn't he care if his words tormented her?

She sighed. Perhaps she could pretend that the day stretching out before her, as lovely and promising as the cloudless sky, was all there would ever be—that tomorrow would never come. In a sense that was true, she realized—this would undoubtedly be the last she and Brandon would ever spend alone together . . . and she wanted all it could hold.

Brandon stared down at the faraway horizon. Despite all his efforts he wasn't making any headway with this infuriatingly determined woman. It was as if he were flying against the force of a stiff headwind that threatened to drive him back, making his goal to have Melissa unattainable. And that *had* become his goal, he admitted resolutely. He wanted her as his wife. But damn it, time was running out. He had to make his move and make it fast. Somehow he had to convince this stubborn little blonde that there was another direction for her life . . . a direction that led to him. He loved her—loved her like he'd never loved another living soul, and he wanted to marry her. But he knew if he pushed her now what her answer would be. And he couldn't accept that. There was no way he was going to lay his cards on the table until he was sure he held the winning hand. But he had today—and damn it, this day was going to count.

"Melissa, give me a chance. I'm not trying to make things difficult for you. I want you to want me as much as I want you."

Taking her hand, he raised it to his lips; reverently, passionately, he kissed it, sending liquid fire through her veins from her throbbing fingertips to her curled toes. Heart pounding erratically, she felt an ache in her throat. His gesture, more intimate than the embrace of lovers, communicated wordlessly a deep longing—his tightening grip communicated an urgency she couldn't resist. Pulling his large hand toward her, the hand that had held hers to his lips, she pressed a moist kiss against his skin. His fist trembled slightly as though with barely contained emotion. She could not keep her tongue from tracing the circle her tingling lips enclosed.

I want you, Brandon, her heart sang, I do! And yet, though filled with the intense inner excitement that swept through her with this silent admission, her throat constricted with the fright of vulnerability, making it impossible for her to speak the words.

Hand in hand, laughing and talking, they walked through the city streets in and out of a wide variety of shops. The quality and type of merchandise varied greatly from gaudy worthless tourist items hawked by street vendors to beautiful imports and handcrafted objets d'art sold in small quiet shops. Soon Brandon's arms were filled with packages and shopping bags as Melissa, in a euphoria of pleasure, expansively bought for those she loved, wanting somehow to share the joy in her heart.

"You've bought something for everyone else," Brandon observed in quiet amusement. "Now it's my turn to buy something for you."

"You don't have to buy me anything, Brandon. Giving me this day is more than enough."

"No, I insist. You must have a souvenir."

Melissa walked by his side as he led her purposefully past shop after shop. Finally, after turning down a sleepy side street, he stopped at a small, surprisingly elegant jewelry store. When they entered the tiny shop, a thin dark man looked up from his work bench. He rose politely, with an air of quiet dignity.

"*Buenos días,* Señor Kade."

"*Buenos días,* Miguel." Brandon deposited the packages he carried on the narrow glass showcase.

Putting his arm possessively around Melissa, drawing her close, Brandon said, "I'd like you to meet Señor Miguel Sánchez, one of the finest jewelers I've met anywhere in the world. Miguel, this is Señora Bennett."

"I'm pleased to meet you, Señor Sánchez," Melissa replied, intrigued by the dark-eyed man before her and the tastefully subdued decor of his shop with its displays of deceptively simple, uniquely artistic pieces of jewelry.

"It is an honor, Señora," Miguel replied. A kindly smile lit his aquiline features. "How may I help you?"

"I'd like to give Señora Bennett a souvenir of her visit to Mexico," Brandon replied, looking briefly at the few items displayed in a small case.

"Do you have any idea what you have in mind?" Miguel asked. "As you know, I generally do custom work, but I have a few other things made up in the safe beyond what you see here." He spread his expressive hands over the lighted case.

"Yes, I do," Brandon said without hesitation. "The last time I stopped in, you showed me a piece you'd been working on in your spare time simply because you wanted the challenge. Do you remember it? It was a pendant replica of the ancient Aztec calendar, I believe."

Miguel's eyes lit up, "Ah, yes. The Sun Stone. If you'll excuse me a moment."

After he left the room, Melissa protested. "Brandon, I really can't accept a valuable gift from you."

"Melissa"—his voice a low husky whisper—"all afternoon I've watched you happily buy things for people who will love receiving a gift they know you've personally chosen for them. This shopping trip has been a first for me. Whenever an occasion calls for a gift my secretary takes care of it. Hell, I'm not always sure what people are thanking me for!"

"But you picked out Brandy and gave her to Jana," Melissa reminded him gently.

"I'd become close enough to her to know what she wanted. It was a real kick for me to be able to give her that dog. But you see, until I met you and your little daughter, there was no one to whom I ever wanted to give a special gift—there was no one to whom I was even close enough to know what they'd *like* to have."

"What about the Raymonds?" Melissa asked, then hesitatingly added, "And Felicia?"

"What could I give the Raymonds other than a token? My standing order is flowers for the ladies and liquor for the judge. And all Felicia ever wanted was a check." One right after the other, he thought wryly, remembering the drain his ex-wife had been on his personal bank account.

"But with you it's different. Everything I see I want to give you. Even more than that, I want you to have something I've longed to give to the right person. And you're the right one, darling." His arms tightened around her as he lowered his face to nuzzle her neck.

Mesmerized by his candor, she felt her cheeks flame crimson. Could his words be true? On this day she wanted to believe that they were.

Miguel returned with a velvet case. Opening it, he revealed the most astonishingly beautiful pendant Melissa had ever seen. Intricately wrought of the finest gold, it was almost three inches in diameter and hung from a heavy handmade golden chain. She gasped with wonder at the sight of the magnificent workmanship and did not resist as Brandon fastened it around her slender neck. Miguel handed her a mirror.

"You're gorgeous! Miguel didn't know it, but he was making that for you," Brandon exclaimed, his expressive face full of emotion.

Melissa felt she was wearing a king's ransom as she looked at the fabulous pendant nestled in the valley above her full breasts. The gold glittered and shone against her tanned smooth skin.

While gazing in the mirror at her reflection, Melissa heard Miguel. "It is a good thing for both of us you came today, Señor. With reluctance I was going to place it with an agent for consignment next week. I cannot afford the luxury of having that much twenty-four-karat gold for myself, and I did want it to be worn instead of hidden away in the safe. I will be honored to know such a lovely woman as the señora is wearing it." Dimly she realized Brandon was paying him for the necklace!

"Brandon, I can't . . ." she protested again. Stopped by the pleading look in his eyes—a look she had never seen there before—she allowed him to purchase the gift, although she knew it went against the dictates of polite society for any woman to accept an expensive gift from a man she was only beginning to know.

Ironically, though Brandon made her feel insignificant and foolish at times, Melissa realized that, conversely, he had the incredible capacity to make her feel cherished and wanted . . . to make her aware and appreciative of her femininity, more completely than anyone else had ever done. She fingered the heavy necklace at her throat, glancing at the powerful man beside her who had given it to her. It was definitely not a bauble or a trinket—the simple souvenir she'd expected. In fact, she was afraid to truly consider just how great the cost had been. She knew he could easily afford it . . . but still . . . She placed the heavy gold back in its resting place in the cleft of her breasts, stroking the soft smooth relief of the Aztec hieroglyphs. No matter what the future held, she knew it would always be her most treasured possession—a rich, unique memento of a man who couldn't give less than the best.

Instead of protesting further she chose simply to savor the moment as if it were fine wine. "Brandon," she murmured, saying the words she knew he needed to hear, "thank you. I love it."

The rest of the day passed in a golden blur. They walked through the twilight to a local restaurant. An old authentic adobe dwelling, it was drab on the outside and seemed to hold little promise, but Melissa was thoroughly delighted as they stepped through the wrought-iron gates into the main courtyard. It was built in the open Spanish style around inner courtyards, with trees growing up through flagstone patios. Brandon and Melissa ate a marvelous meal seated at a heavy trestle table under the open sky as the bright flaming dusk turned to a velvet dark studded with the brilliance of distant stars.

Pleasantly aware of the strolling mariachi band that entertained in the background, they talked together of their interests in books, music, movies, and plays. Bit by revealing bit, Melissa came to know and understand the self-motivating drive of the man before her as she encouraged him to talk of his childhood ambitions and dreams.

In answer to her question as to how he became a jet pilot, he spoke softly. "From the moment I first became aware of them as a child I was fascinated by the planes that flew high over our valley in the Appalachian hills. It seems I knew even then that I had to hitch my future to something that would get me out of there. I knew I was going to be one of the men who flew those planes. My dad told me only college boys could fly, so I determined then and there I'd get to college somehow. Actually I was the only one in my family to get through high school. When I was eighteen, I hitchhiked to Philadelphia and got a basketball scholarship at the University of Pennsylvania. I joined the Air Force ROTC and from there realized my dream to fly a jet."

Melissa didn't want the evening to end. Her dinner was virtually untouched, but her appetite to learn more about Brandon Kade was insatiable. "And the Raymonds, where did you meet them?" she asked, sipping a salt-rimmed margarita.

"I pictured myself a modern day Ben Franklin when I arrived in Philly," he smiled, flashing even white teeth. "Whatever spare time I could find, I spent in the courts observing the lawyers. Since all the truly great men in our history had started out as lawyers, I figured that was the path for me. After a while I became aware that one judge had more on the ball than any of the others; that judge was Warren Raymond. I became a permanent fixture in the courtroom whenever he was presiding. One day he sent a clerk to ask me back to his chambers. Unbelievably, he asked my opinion about a case that had been argued, and on which he had reached, but not yet announced, a verdict. I guess he was impressed with my amateur reasoning, because from then on he took me under his wing.

"And speaking of wings, it's time we were flying home, much as I'd like to stay here with you," Brandon murmured regretfully, rising to pull out her chair. Package-laden, he put his free hand on the small of her back, signaling a growing intimacy.

On the return trip in the darkness of the evening sky, Brandon put his arm around Melissa, drawing her close to him, allowing no distance to separate them. Nestling her head against his broad shoulder, she couldn't remember ever being happier. Why did this perfect day have to end? Why did she and this wonderful man, for whom she now cared deeply and who she was sure cared for her in return, have to have so many differences and obstacles to happiness in their path? Why did life have to be so complicated? she wondered silently. She turned her head to look at him more closely, and he smiled down at her. Her heart melted and she again made the promise to herself to live the moment. What more could she ask for? she wondered, pushing all other thoughts from her mind.

After landing they were met by a customs official and asked if they had anything to declare. Brandon handed him the receipts from the packages and indicated the necklace Melissa wore.

"I have the receipt for that, too, but before I make the declaration I'll escort the lady to my car." The commanding man gestured to the lot just next to the customs shed.

"That's fine, Mr. Kade." The guard nodded his assent to this unorthodox request. "I'll meet you inside."

At the car Brandon gently cupped her face in his large hands; then Melissa felt the giddy, heady sensation of his persuasive lips burning against the softness of hers. "Don't go anywhere, baby—I'll be right back," he said, firmly closing the passenger door.

After stowing the packages in the trunk, he strode briskly to the customs building. Melissa watched through open venetian blinds as he stood in harsh fluorescent light filling out the necessary forms. When she saw him reach for his wallet to pay the duty tax, she knew the dreamy day was over. With the payment of the duty, the word itself sent out a warning—harsh reality struck. The heavy gold chain with its elaborate pendant suddenly weighed upon her neck like a burden—a burden of inherent obligation that demanded a reciprocal gift.

When he returned to the car and slid behind the wheel, Melissa couldn't contain a rising sense of anxiety.

"Brandon?"

"Yes?" He expertly backed the car out of the parking space and shifted gear. "What is it?"

The nagging of her conscience continued. "I shouldn't have allowed you to give me the necklace."

"Why? Don't you like it?"

"How can you ask that? It's beautiful. The workmanship is the finest I've ever seen. But I know it must be far too valuable . . ." She bit her lip, a cold knot twisting in her stomach, uncertain as to how to say what she knew she must. "I—I don't know what you expect in return," she stammered, floundering in her discomfort, thankful the darkness of the car concealed her furious blush.

Abruptly turning the car to the side of the street, he pulled to a stop. "Is that what you think? That I gave the necklace to you as a bribe? That it comes with an account payable clause?" He looked at her in sincere disbelief. "What you must think of me, Melissa." He shook his head, then sat silently a few moments, head bent down, his wrists resting on the top of the steering wheel.

Finally he turned, took her hands in his, and said in a surprisingly gentle voice, "I'll tell you what I expect in return: I expect the very real pleasure of seeing it around your beautiful throat when I'm with you and of knowing you have it to wear when I'm not. Is that so difficult for you to understand and accept?"

Remorseful, Melissa felt foolish and ridiculous. She wanted to believe he really meant what he was saying. "I'm sorry, Brandon. I may still know how to give gifts, but I guess I've forgotten how to accept them gracefully."

"I don't want an apology, honey," he said, his voice hushed, drawling. His use of the unfamiliar endearment caused her to shiver as he put his hand under her chin, turning her face to his. "If and when anything happens between us, it won't be bought and paid for. I want it to be because we both want it and for no other reason."

His hurt-filled eyes seemed to burn into her soul. Looking

at him, Melissa realized he was being completely candid. A delicious tingle of anticipation and excitement ran through her when she thought of Brandon Kade wanting her, truly desiring her. She knew she longed to be in his arms—uninhibited and free of constraint. Why had she thrown up this ill-timed barrier of misunderstanding between them?

Clothed in the sheerest of gowns, Melissa stepped out onto the small balcony to let the cool refreshing balm of the sea breeze bathe her heated overwrought body. The clear warm night closed around her, pulsing in a symphony of hushed harmonious sounds, the rasping whisper of nearby palms almost lost in the more distant swelling surge of the rippling sea—its muted eternal roar seemed to echo the tumult and confusion in her breast. Mingled perfumes of luxurious tropical blossoms wafted fragrantly on the air, impelling her to breathe deeply, savoring their elusive yet all-pervasive scents. In that sweet moment of unreality, vibrant awareness of the essence of life overcame her. Her dreamy senses grasped one essential truth: without a doubt, she had fallen in love with Brandon Kade.

Resting folded bare arms on the wrought-iron railing, she let this truth command her thoughts, dictate her emotions. She was in love with a man almost as powerful as the mighty ocean that beat below her; in love with a man as sensuous and enticing as the exotic blooms that sent on the willing breeze their intoxicating invitations to love.

Hopelessly in love though she might be, what could she hope for from him? That he would love her in return? Perhaps he did love her in his own way, but enough to overcome the obstacles that lay between them? A painful remnant, a fleeting vignette of their first meeting, caught in her mind. Could he possibly love her enough to rethink his views on so much that was vitally important to her? Absently fingering the medallion at her breast, she remembered that family was not a high priority on his list of life's pleasures or rewards; he'd already made himself quite clear on that point. Yet there was no doubt in her mind that he felt more for her than simple sexual attraction.

Could he also be experiencing the restless need that had been opening like a bottomless chasm deep within her soul? A nameless need that had not existed until they'd met? There were no answers to these questions, she realized, running her fingers lightly through her sun-bleached hair. She knew only that life without Brandon Kade was flat, barely two dimensional. She wasn't sure she could ever have a full life as a woman without the added depth of his love. Unconsciously she lifted the heavy golden medallion to her soft lips. Had he meant the medallion to be merely a costly souvenir? Was this episode to end with no more than mementos to remind her of him?

Her dreamy reverie was abruptly disturbed by an urgent yet subdued tapping on the door of her suite. It was very late, too late, she had thought, for Julia to expect their usual nightly chat. The house had been completely quiet and the upstairs windows dark when she and Brandon had returned from Mexico. Perhaps Julia couldn't wait until morning to hear how the day had gone, she sighed, as she left the solitary peacefulness of the balcony.

Quietly opening the door she let out a startled gasp when she saw Brandon, the deep V of his maroon velour robe exposing a mat of dark curly hair above the tie of his waist, his feet bare.

"I can't sleep, Melissa," he whispered. "Let's walk down by the water." He caught her hand in his, drawing her into the thickly carpeted hall, silently shutting the door behind her. Captivated, unwilling to utter an empty protest, she let herself be pulled down the staircase, then outside toward the walkway to the beach.

The incredibly beautiful darkness, its fathomless, infinitely distant midnight blue sky awash with twinkling stars, concealed their flight toward the strand. A descending moon spread a broken path of silver upon the rolling waves. As they walked hand in hand through the glow of the moonlight, Melissa saw the sand of the deserted beach sparkle in answer to the stars above. In the freshly blowing sulfurous salt-tanged air a lone lighthouse stood sentinel, shooting the revolving sweep of its beam out to sea. Her senses alive to the beauty of the scene, she knew the night was only a backdrop to an empty stage waiting for some compelling drama to unfold.

As if enchanted, she felt his steps slow to a stop. She felt herself being pulled into the circle of Brandon's enveloping arms, felt her heart hammer against his as her passion-weakened body pressed against his strength. Her filmy nightgown swirled, dancing wraithlike around her in the soft breeze. Caught in the heady romance of the moment, ready to mindlessly express her newly realized love for him, she raised her face to receive his kiss, lifting her arms to his broad shoulders to hold him closer, wanting to transmit to his lean hard body the soft warmth and glow of hers. Slowly he bent, until his lips were almost touching hers. In agonizing sweetness she waited for his embrace to consume her, as his arms tightened, and finally his mouth melted into hers.

The unbearable tension that had been mounting between them during the day found fierce release in the joyous coming together of their beings—an ardorous intertwining of their breath, their lips, their tongues, their bodies, in an embrace at once demanding and seeking, as well as responding and giving. It was a kiss from which Melissa knew there was no holding back, no breaking away.

In a moment of complete abandon she felt her soul released from the constraints of her body; she felt it spiraling upward on the silver light of the moon. Upwards it traveled, coursing through the universe. She did not feel her gown being pulled over her head, uncomprehendingly she saw it softly billow away to the sand, leaving her standing unashamedly naked except, significantly, for the heavy gold pendant gleaming between her upturned breasts. She did not know that her curvaceous body shone as luminescent as the waves upon the shore in the moonlight. She saw only the way Brandon's eyes hungrily drank in the sight of her.

His husky voice whispered, "You're as perfect as I imagined." His eyes slowly explored her figure as his hand traced a sensuous line down her throat. "Your breasts . . ." His hand faltered, touching her reverently, tenderly, sending a wave of sensation beating excitedly within her. His hand left her breast to travel a maddeningly sensuous path to her slim waist and then down the womanly swell of her hips, causing her to moan, to call out his name.

"You feel like satin," he murmured. His voice caught on the words as his hands slid around her back, cupping her hips, clasping her almost spasmodically to him, crushing her mouth with his, drawing from her the certain knowledge that she wanted him as badly as he wanted her.

The long passionate kiss left them both breathless yet yearning for more. Inexplicably he pulled back, his body no longer touching hers, yet his radiating heat continued to fuel her fiery desire. His penetrating eyes held hers as he dropped his robe to the white sand. Briefly he stood there illuminated in the pale light as perfect and shapely as a Greek statue—wide-shouldered, deep-chested, slip-hipped—the powerful muscles of his thighs slimming to the rounded masculine calves of his long legs. After indulging her eyes with his male beauty, Melissa closed the distance between them, and with exquisite pleasure and a sense of female power she felt him shudder as the aroused tips of her breasts met the bareness of his chest.

Gently he lowered her to his outspread robe, and as he lay beside her, he teasingly traced the curves of her body. His musky odor merged with the intoxicating aroma of her womanly scent.

"This is the moment I've been dreaming about—willing to happen—the moment when I would see in your eyes the desire for me that I feel for you." His drawling voice was low, deep. "Melissa, do you want it to happen? Do you want me to stop? Say it. I must hear you say you want me."

She looked up into his rapturous face so close to hers, slowly, completely, marveling at the noble symmetry of his strong high cheekbones, the heavy lashes framing his intense blue eyes, the firm fullness of his expressive lips, the whiteness of his strong, straight teeth, the squareness of his sturdy chin with its barely perceptible cleft. She lightly traced the outline of his lips with the tip of her finger. The pounding of her heart drowning out the sound of the surf, she reached up, clasping her hands behind his strong neck, and pulled his mouth to hers in a long searching embrace.

"I want you." Her lips finally mouthed the words against his.

Letting out a low growl full of primitive meaning, he put his arms around her waist as he bent to kiss the fullness of her breasts. Her hands gloriously ran through his hair and on down, exploring, feeling for herself the coiled power of his muscular back. His ardor increased at the inviting touch of her kneading hands. Pushing aside the golden pendant, his warm mouth hungrily, greedily, sought her sensitized nipples while his hand surely moved to caress the soft silkiness of her throbbing belly. The sky tilted crazily above her and the stars seemed to pulse, then explode into a fabulous display of cosmic fireworks. Shivering in anticipation, she responded instinctively, her hips writhing.

His mouth found hers—insistently, urgently probing its sweet depths. Swept by the wave of passion, her body arched tautly toward his; every nerve of her being yearned for his penetration. Afire with passion, he slid his hand lower, caressing the beating pulse between her thighs, causing an ecstasy of sensation to explode within her. Her hands grasped the rock-hard flesh of his buttocks, urging his body into hers. They came together in a rhythm as natural and timeless as the ebb and flow of the sea beside them.

The moon slowly sank into the sea, taking with it the silver pathway to the shore. The night darkened around them, and the stars shone with greater brilliance, but they didn't notice. Each was absorbed, consumed in giving the greatest pleasure possible to the other. The rapture of their consummation was complete as they gave unselfishly in the pureness of their love, their bodies fitting as though they had been made only for this moment. They stayed on the beach sharing the unceasing ecstasy of their delight until the coming of the rosy dawn began to drive away the stars overhead.

At Melissa's door, Brandon held her possessively once more, whispering, "Snowbird, you belong to me now."

She could only murmur "Yes, yes" against his passion-bruised lips.

CHAPTER EIGHT

The day of Julia's wedding dawned clear and bright. Before sunrise, caterers had begun setting up on the lawn that had been groomed to give the appearance of plush green carpeting. Brightly striped awnings, a polished temporary wooden dance floor, chairs, buffet tables, and a beautiful flower-entwined arbor under which Julia and Scott would say their vows sprung up as if by magic. By midafternoon the orchestra had arrived, and strains of music filled the air as they rehearsed under the shade of a shell-shaped canopy.

By four o'clock the distinguished assemblage of guests was seated in an area under huge arching cypresses, the trees' majestic presence giving the feeling of a large outdoor chapel. The poised orchestra struck up the overture, and rich music filled the air.

The wedding procession began as a robed clergyman led the groom and his men, handsome in their traditional black tuxedoes, to their places. Bridesmaids, lovely in long graceful mauve gowns, carrying orchids on silk fans, slowly walked down the aisle in step to the music to take their places beside the sweetly perfumed floral arbor.

Distinctively dressed in a tiny-strapped, muted plum, low V-necked gown that complemented her delicate complexion, Melissa, the matron of honor, came into view. The hem of her full skirt, cut up in sharp points to her knees, reached to her slender ankles. Over the bodice a filmy long-sleeved overblouse, which was trimmed with lace and gathered in at the waist, cut to a sharp downward point in the front. She carried an antique lace fan laden with exquisite pink and plum-toned orchids. Melissa had to agree with Julia's assessment, that it was probably the most flattering outfit she'd ever worn. She felt wholly elegant from the matching plum-colored cap that smartly dipped to a point over her brow to the wispy ankle-strapped plum sandals that lightly encased her small feet. Rosy pink pearl studs, a gift from Julia, glowed from the lobes of her small well-formed ears.

As she walked down the aisle, she felt Brandon's eyes upon her and colored faintly. Surrounded by a sea of faces turned toward her, Melissa could see only one . . . her warm smile, her love-filled eyes were only for one. Could the others see it on her face? she wondered fleetingly. Had their union left an invisible but perceptible brand that marked them as lovers? When Brandon stepped forward to offer his arm and they approached the fragrant arbor together, Melissa's heart sang with a joy as true as that she knew Julia must be feeling.

Before releasing her, Brandon gently squeezed her hand to his chest, whispering huskily, "You are so very, very beautiful." Vainly she tried to suppress, or at least control, the sensuous smile that spread across her face as she looked into his eyes, vividly remembering the last time he'd said those words.

Lost in a romantic haze, Melissa relived the starlit night they had spent on the beach consummating their unspoken love, until she saw her tiny daughter. Dressed in a full-length white lace dress, a wreath of baby's breath entwined with pink tea roses encircling her head, Jana blithely scattered rose petals on the red-carpeted aisle. Watching her, Melissa thought her heart would burst with happiness and maternal pride.

The orchestra's change in key announced the arrival of the bride. Everyone rose and turned to where Julia, fabulously clad in her long white wedding gown and looking radiantly happy beneath her gossamer veil, serenely glided down the aisle on the arm of her distinguished father. She was a vision in soft chiffon, shimmering satin, and aerial lace, carrying a cascading bouquet of white orchids and stephanotis.

The traditional wedding ceremony proceeded faultlessly. Tears of happiness glistened in the eyes of many women in the audience as they recalled their own weddings and reached over to take the hands of the men they had married on long-ago summer days. A tender feeling of closeness was transmuted through this almost universal act as their husbands responded warmly to the tangible expression of the ties that bound them.

As Scott claimed Julia with a kiss under the orange blossom, jasmine, and gardenia laden arbor, Melissa sensed Brandon's searing gaze before her eyes were drawn to his. Pulse pounding, she vividly remembered the exquisitely unique torment of his hard masculine body taking absolute possession of hers. Her skin tingled, burned, remembering the intimate touch of his knowing hands and mouth caressing, arousing her senses to fever pitch. Feeling weak, she raised her orchid-covered fan to her face in an unconsciously charming gesture, hoping to hide the flush that spread into her cheeks and the smile upon her lips that the blatant boldness of his eyes had evoked.

The bride and groom made a startlingly handsome couple as arm in arm they triumphantly went up the aisle to the strains of the recessional. The stunning matron of honor on the arm of the dashingly handsome best man made no less a pleasing and dramatic impression.

It was several moments before the guests, still held in the spell of the breathtakingly beautiful ceremony, rose from their seats to proceed up the aisle and out onto the lawn where a reception line had formed. Content, feeling a strong sense of belonging, Melissa stood between Brandon and Grace as she was introduced to those guests she hadn't already met and greeted the many others who now seemed almost like friends.

Champagne flowed from a sparkling crystal fountain, and a lavish buffet was spread out on long white linen-covered tables. Carved ice sculptures holding seafood and fresh fruits served as glistening centerpieces for each table. Waiters constantly circulated among the guests, busily replacing empty glasses with full. The band struck up a time-honored waltz as Julia and Scott romantically danced the first number, soon joined by their parents, formally opening the festivities.

Brandon, who had never left Melissa's side, masterfully swept her into his arms, swirling her onto the dance floor as soon as protocol would allow.

"The past two days have been hell," he growled meaningfully. "I was beginning to think I'd never hold you in my arms again. If I thought no one would notice, I'd kiss your luscious lips right here."

"Somehow, I think someone would," Melissa murmured with a smile, suddenly conscious of the attention they were attracting. Brandon Kade was not the kind of man who could escape notice in any crowd. His custom-tailored tuxedo skimmed the long lines of his body perfectly—the white shirt with its black-rimmed ruffles emphasized his deep tan and even teeth, causing his eyes to appear a clear true blue. His was not a case of the clothes making the man, Melissa thought with a secret shiver of delight. How well she knew his body needed no tailored covering to mask flaws or shortcomings. His muscular frame, stately and ideal in its proportions, excellent in its symmetry, was flawless—without blemish. Melissa was sure that every female present, no matter how contented in her own sexual relationship, longed with at least a small inner part of her emotions to be the object of Brandon Kade's desire.

"Every time I tried to get away from that damned bachelor party someone proposed a toast, or another girl jumped out of a cake," he joked.

Melissa's eyes widened. "How many girls were there?"

"After a while, I lost count." He smiled wryly. "Two or three apiece, I suppose."

"Even for the judge and Scott's father?" She almost missed a step.

"Showgirls seem to go for white-haired men," he shrugged, laughing at her shocked expression. "I'm just kidding, honey. Besides, even if there'd been a dozen for each of us, I wouldn't have noticed. I only had one little blonde on my mind. But there was no way I could get out of there." His lips nuzzled the hair above her ear.

"And last night, after the rehearsal dinner, this place was like a damned hotel. There were so many bridesmaids running around, I was afraid to knock on your door for fear they might have bunked one in with you and Jana."

Melissa laughed, swaying with the music, feeling secure wrapped in his powerful embrace. "Poor darling, I missed you too."

"After we drop Scott and Julia at the airport, *we're* going to take the *long* way home. We need some time to talk." His meaning was unmistakable, yet subtle with implications. But Melissa had no time to dwell on them. The mention of Julia's name had reminded Melissa of her duties as matron of honor. She glanced around the crowd until she saw Julia. The bride beckoned to her.

"Oh, Brandon, I'd almost forgotten. It's getting late, and I have to help Julia out of her gown. Dance me over there to meet her."

"I'll be waiting. Just don't take too long." Brandon briefly tightened his hold on her before letting go, his hand slipping down her arm, lingering in a short handclasp, as though he couldn't bear to lose contact.

Together she and Julia entered the hushed quiet of the house. In Julia's room there wasn't much time to talk, but the two friends clung to each other for an emotion-filled embrace as they realized their lives had been irrevocably changed by the events of the past few hours.

"I think these are what Mother calls 'happy tears,' " Julia said, smiling as she and Melissa dried their eyes.

"I'll remember that," Melissa replied softly. "I'll remember everything about this fabulous summer—and I'll never forget the the best friend I've ever had."

"Me too." Julia's eyes misted again as the two friends fondly hugged once more. Strains of music floated up from below, where lanterns had begun to glow softly in the darkening recesses of the trees.

After Melissa helped Julia from her lovely gown, she went to her own room, where she changed into a crisp linen dress. She could still feel the strength in Brandon's arms, holding her close to him as they'd danced. She'd felt cherished, protected . . . and even loved, very loved . . . as he'd publicly, in front of his friends and colleagues, demonstrated his possession of her. Her skin flushed with a warm glow as she remembered again the ultimate passion they'd shared. How perfect . . . how dreamlike it had been in the warmth of the summer night.

Was the dream drawing to a close? Or was she to find her happy ending tonight? She'd thought of little else in the past two days. Why—she shook her head in wonder—why did I have to meet Brandon right now? She had so much to resolve before she could incorporate another person into her life. She was just beginning to build the foundations for her resumed life with Jana. That had to come first in her priorities . . . and Laurence was still expecting her to return, to take the position he'd made for her in his firm. She was keenly aware of her obligation to him, and until she'd met Brandon, she'd been more than willing to fulfill it on his terms.

What she needed right now, she thought with a deep sigh, was a little time and a great deal of understanding from the marvelous man she'd fallen in love with. Brandon had said they needed to talk. Instinctively, she felt he planned to propose marriage. And that was what she wanted . . . wanted with all her heart. But she still desperately needed time. She couldn't throw her past to the wind without a backward glance. What she had to come away with on this night, before she left for Anchorage, was a firm declaration of Brandon's love and his willingness to wait for her.

Her father-in-law adored her and Jana—in time she was sure he could be made to understand that Brandon was the man she needed for a husband and Jana needed for a father. It would be very difficult for Laurence to accept the separation this would cause, but she was sure once he understood that their bond of love and family would never be broken or weakened, he would come around. Brandon had certainly come a long way in his understanding of her devotion to her daughter—surely he could come to understand her devotion to Laurence Bennett. At least Brandon's love for Jana was unqualified, she was sure of that. Perhaps it all wasn't as impossibly difficult as it had once seemed, Melissa thought hopefully, quickly freshening her makeup.

But even if they could work out the family problems, what about her career? Was it that much of a stumbling block, after all? Brandon hadn't referred to her need for independence since she'd explained her feelings about it that night in Anaheim. Perhaps, after thinking about it, he had come to understand that too. Surely, knowing the personal sacrifices she'd made in order to obtain her law degree, and realizing the intellectually stimulating climate in which she'd lived for the last three years, he understood that she could never happily return to a life in which law wasn't an integral part.

Brandon loved her—she could see it in his eyes, hear it in his voice. And she loved him. Loved him enough to make compromises . . . to work things out so that they could be together . . . loved him enough to meet him halfway. All of the men in her experience—her own father, Sonny, and Laurence—had been wholly masculine . . . even domineering at times. But they'd had one important quality in common: when it came down to it, they'd been ready to accommodate the needs of the women they'd loved. Surely Brandon couldn't be any less a man. Heartened, she quickly dabbed rose lipstick on her lips and hurried from the room.

Melissa didn't want to be a part of the semicircle of unmarried women expectantly waiting in front of the door for Julia to throw her bouquet, but Grace left her no choice, taking her by the arm, thrusting a packet of rice into her hand and maneuvering her into their group. When Grace had intercepted her, Melissa had been trying to make her way through the crowd to where Brandon was standing, leaning against the waiting car parked across the drive in front of the spectacular backdrop of the mosaic pool and fountain. Meeting his eyes through the crowd, hope for the promise of the evening surged within her breast.

As Julia and Scott emerged arm in arm from the mansion, they were met with a hail of rice. Julia paused for a moment, her eyes searching the boisterous crowd of competitive girls. Finding Melissa's petite form near the the back of the group, Julia aimed directly for where her friend stood, tossing her bouquet high into the air. Her aim was right on the mark. When the cascade of flowers came straight down toward Melissa, Grace reached up eagerly to help her catch it.

Putting her arm around Melissa, Grace smiled knowingly. "I'm sure you'll be next," she said happily, glancing toward Brandon.

Melissa was too unnerved to reply. Making her way through the well-wishers, she reached the car and shifted the bouquet to one arm as she held the door open for Scott and Julia, waiting while Grace and Warren gave their daughter a last hug and kiss.

At the airport Scott and Brandon took care of the luggage and tickets while Melissa and Julia shared a final few minutes together.

"Be good to Brandon, please. You haven't told me how you feel about him, but I know he cares for you. He's always had a difficult time showing his real feelings, but you've helped him become more tender and caring. Both Scott and I have noticed a marked difference in him since you came into his life.

"You care for him too, don't you, Melissa?" Julia asked softly.

"Yes," Melissa admitted, "but . . ."

"Our flight for Tahiti is boarding right now, Mrs. Lowell," Scott announced. The two young women had been so engrossed in conversation they hadn't noticed the approach of the men. "Come on, let's not miss our honeymoon."

"Just a second, darling." Julia turned back to Melissa, whispering, "No buts. It'll all work out—you'll see." They embraced quickly as Brandon and Scott shook hands.

Brandon looked down at the small blond head of the beautiful woman walking beside him, her hand trustingly in his. When he'd seen her—a vision of ideal feminine beauty—coming down the aisle that afternoon, the breath had literally stopped in his throat. He'd made up his mind then and there to ask her to marry him tonight. An intense longing had swept over him, and for an instant the insane notion to step forward to ask the clergyman to perform a double ceremony had flashed briefly through his love-sodden mind. He smiled wryly, without humor, as he thought of the commotion that would have caused in the well-planned proceedings!

But . . . he didn't want to live without her. It had been difficult to keep from asking her to marry him even as they'd danced, but he'd checked his words, wanting that moment to be theirs alone. How he wished that it were he and Melissa flying off to a lush tropical island, as unencumbered and free as Julia and Scott.

But as it stood now, if Melissa and he planned to marry, there were so many obstacles to surmount in their path to wedded bliss that it seemed damned near impossible. By the time they had argued their differences out, they would probably not only not end up at the altar but would end up bitter enemies. Damn it, why hadn't he had the good sense to fall in love with a woman who'd happily fit into his life-style? Why had he fallen for an independent little number, with a family in Alaska, who wanted a career of her own? A *law* career at that! *She* couldn't be an interior decorator or a dress designer. Oh, no! *She* had to be an aspiring attorney!

He slammed her car door a little harder than he'd intended, causing her to look up at him with a puzzled expression. Hell, he thought with remorse, he didn't want to hurt her. All he wanted was to take her in his arms, fly her and Jana with him back to San Francisco, and spend the rest of his life making her happy. But damn it! *She* was the one who didn't want that. *She* was the one insisting that they had problems. He started the car and drove down the circular ramp leading out of the parking garage, rapidly enough to cause the tires to screech unpleasantly. Well, maybe that wasn't a fair assessment. They did have problems, he admitted. Too damn many problems.

There was no way he could propose to her as he'd planned. He needed time . . . and space. He'd grown too attached to her. Maybe if he let her return to Alaska, he'd come to his senses and get over her. Lord, he groaned inwardly, thinking of the beauty of the womanly body, luminescent in the moonlight, that had given him the greatest physical pleasure he'd ever known in anyone's arms—thinking of the beautiful smile and glowing sapphire eyes that caused his heart to sing—thinking of the subtle wit and gentle kindness of her multifaceted personality that both challenged and consoled him . . . how in the hell could he ever consider giving all that up? He had to, he told himself resolutely, with a jagged flash of grief—given all the givens, he was left with no real choice. As difficult as it was for him to accept, they just weren't meant for each other. He had to set her free.

Melissa glanced at the man sitting at her side—he'd suddenly become a stranger. He seemed almost angry, his face darkened with inner thoughts, a muscle working in the corner of his strong jaw. What had caused the volatile mood shift, that was so unlike him? she wondered, with a rising sense of anxiety. Had she said something? She couldn't imagine what.

"It was a beautiful wedding," Melissa remarked with a casualness she didn't feel, hoping to find that her fears were unfounded.

The red sun slowly sank into the sea, coloring the water gold and purple; a soft ocean breeze blew over the warm land as Brandon, impassively making no comment, wheeled the car to the side of the road and parked along the strand.

She waited expectantly for the moment when he would pull her to him and kiss her with the mounting urgency that had been building between them for days. But when he remained with his hands on the wheel, she took the initiative, drawing his arm around her, nestling herself against his broad chest, lightly slipping his hand under the surplice neckline of her dress. Instead of the fondling response she expected, his hand rested heavily, inertly on the smooth swell of her breast, although a slight tremor passed over his body, indicating some kind of great inner turmoil.

"What's the matter, Brandon?" she asked as they watched the sun slip into the sea and twilight spread around them.

"Weddings make me nervous," Brandon said seriously, breaking his silence at last, a note of gruffness in his usually smooth voice.

"Yes, you did act a little jittery when you gave the ring to Scott. I was afraid you might drop it." She smiled at the memory, her hand distractedly smoothing the fine fabric of his blazer sleeve.

"It isn't that part so much," he said, unwilling to voice his true concerns, "as all the folderol that goes into it: the months of planning, the time each guest gives up for the wedding, and the elaborate expense of the whole thing to celebrate something that might not even last."

Melissa stiffened and pulled away from him.

"What do you mean, might not last? Do you think Julia and Scott will have trouble in their marriage?" She turned to face him, alarmed at his remark, her pure blue eyes glinting.

"Well"—he shrugged carelessly, choosing his comments deliberately—"if Julia's sensible and puts her energies into supporting Scott in his career, they may buck the odds and make it fine. But the way things stand now, I'd say their marriage is in trouble before it starts." He added bitterly, "Two careers don't make a happy marriage."

Appalled, Melissa pushed herself completely free, her hands against his chest. She knew he had to have been affected by his divorce, but she'd never before seen any sign of this deep-seated bitterness.

"Careers don't cause divorces, Brandon. People do. From what Julia told me, Felicia never really wanted a marriage in the true sense," she said gently, her voice full with kindness. "You mustn't use your unfortunate experience as a yardstick to measure the probability of the success or failure of other marriages."

"That's a condescending statement coming from you," he shot back cuttingly.

"What do you mean?" she asked, suddenly realizing the extent of his hostility.

"You use your late husband's lack of consideration for your future as your justification for your need to remain independent of any man. Now you're attributing my feelings about Julia and Scott to the failure of my marriage. My marriage has nothing to do with this. I'm surprised that you'd throw that colossal error in judgment up in my face," he parried angrily.

"I didn't mean to do anything like that," Melissa apologized, hiding the hurt she felt. How could such a perfect day end in a senseless fight when there was so little time left for them to come to any kind of understanding? A nameless uneasiness grew in the back of her mind as she realized just how much was at stake here.

She tried once more. "Brandon, don't you think if Julia and Scott love one another enough they can work it all out? I think they have discussed the future—from what Julia's told me they've already reached agreement on many vital issues."

Brandon let out a dismissing huff of air. "I know all about that. Scott's told me the same naïve thing. But once lovers come down from their dreamy towers to face the harsh realities of real life, things look very different. I predict the two of them won't be any exception."

Melissa's heart skipped a beat. "Brandon," she asked softly, "are we talking about Julia and Scott . . . or you and me?"

His silence was an answer, confirming her growing fears. What a fool she had been to think loving her had changed him in the least! She realized with a dreadful certainty, which twisted like a cold knife in her heart, that he would never understand what she had to do with her life. . . . Her budding hopes dashed, it was some time before she recovered enough to reply—finally forcing a steadiness into her voice that her tumultuous emotions threatened to destroy.

"You don't have a thing to worry about. I'd never consider marrying you with the archaic ideas you hold about women and their right to fulfillment." Her eyes narrowed to slits.

"No one asked you to." His rapier reply, spoken in glacial tones, erected a frozen invisible wall between them.

His face took on a hard, grim set. It was done. But her beauty saturated his senses, almost driving him mad; he couldn't allow himself to remember that it was he who had caused the pain that he saw in her tear-filled eyes, eyes that sparkled like jewels through a mist. He longed to take her wonderfully soft feminine body in his arms and kiss away the hurt, erase the pain. But he steeled himself against her almost irresistible appeal. It was better to break the green, growing tendrils of love now, before it was too late . . . before they ended up having to dig out and discard the bitter, broken roots of a full-blown involvement. Perhaps this way, in time, they could both look back at their affair, happy memories still intact. He abruptly started the engine without another word. He stepped on the accelerator sharply, and the car took off with a spin of gravel, throwing Melissa back against the leather upholstery of the seat.

Tears blinded her eyes. It was over. Her heart screamed, remembering the hope it had held just hours before, but her lips were sealed, mute. The words that he'd chosen had been just that. Chosen to leave no doubt in her mind that it was just as she'd thought in the beginning: she'd been nothing more to him than a summer's fling, a pleasant diversion . . . a doll to be used and cast aside.

Julia's elegant bouquet lay forlornly forgotten on the backseat as Melissa ran from the car into the house, tears streaming down her face. Fortunately she encountered no one as she stumbled up the steps and closed the door to her room. Throwing herself on the bed, she began to sob. The sound of the ocean, its waves breaking inexorably on the shore, offered her broken heart no solace this night.

The next day an organized turmoil of activity buzzed on the lawn as the caterers dismantled and packed away the reception paraphernalia. Jana, outside early, helped Warren supervise, as the dogs jumped and ran around the workers, making the job more difficult. In the brilliant sunlight it was still possible to imagine the festive scene of the day before. In stark contrast, inside, the huge house lay ominously quiet. Grace, uncharacteristically apathetic, slowly wandered from room to room, straightening a chair here or a rug there.

When Melissa appeared late in the morning, traces of the intermittent crying that had racked her body during the night were still apparent on her face. Seeing the sadness in Grace's eyes, she knew she would have to pull herself together and help Grace face the emptiness that she must be feeling.

"Oh, there you are." Grace managed a feeble smile. "Didn't you sleep well, dear? Your face looks a little puffy." Not waiting for an answer, she went on, "You must be hungry. I'll tell Maria to serve your breakfast on the patio."

"Thank you, but I'm really not. Just coffee will be fine," Melissa said, trying to smile in return.

They sat down together at the white wrought-iron glass-topped table that was already set. Grace poured a cup for each of them from the insulated pot and then settled back into the flowered cushions of her chair, holding a cup and saucer in her hands.

"The house feels so empty now with Julia and Scott and Brandon gone . . ." Melissa wasn't really listening as she noticed how much older Grace looked than she had ever seemed before. "It's going to be impossible when you and Jana leave." Grace sighed glumly.

"Is Brandon gone?" Melissa's eyes widened perceptively. When at last the meaning of Grace's words had sunk through, the question had popped from her mouth unthinkingly.

"Yes, he left quite early, after breakfasting with Jana. He explained that when he called San Francisco this morning, his secretary informed him of an urgent matter that required his immediate return." Grace took a sip of her coffee. "Actually there was a taxi waiting for him at the door when he came to tell Warren and me. Brandon's a busy man, very much in demand."

Unwilling, and absolutely unable, to listen to what she feared might turn into a discussion of Brandon Kade's attributes, Melissa deliberately changed the subject.

"It was a beautiful wedding," she said mechanically. With a jolt of pain the words echoed in her mind. She remembered with searing agony the episode that had developed the last time she'd said them.

"And Julia looked lovelier than I've ever seen her. She and Scott make the perfect couple." Melissa realized she was rambling, stating the obvious to cover her own devastating confusion. But Grace didn't seem to notice; she absently nodded in agreement, her mind obviously far away.

Abruptly, Grace put down her cup and rose from the table. "Excuse me for a moment," she said. "I've just thought of something important I want to discuss with Warren."

Melissa felt bleak and forsaken—utterly deserted. Her resolve to forget him melted into despair. How she wished she could dismiss him from her mind—wipe out the memory of his hauntingly unforgettable face, his possessive arms, his intimate embraces, his burning kisses. He was gone—gone as irrevocably as last night's sunset. Somehow she would have to live without him. She had to admit she had always known, deep down inside of her, that their affair, wonderful though it had been, had been hopeless from the start.

Grace returned to the patio carrying Julia's bouquet tenderly cradled to her bosom. "I found this in the front hall, dear." A quizzical look of vague reproach filled her eyes.

Thoughts of the bouquet had not entered Melissa's mind since she'd carefully laid it on the backseat of the car the night before. Knowing the sentimental meaning the flowers had for Grace, she was stricken with remorse that Julia's mother had been the one to find it, seemingly thoughtlessly cast aside. She remembered how sweet Grace had been when she'd helped her catch it, only hours before.

"Oh, Grace, I'm so sorry. I must have forgotten it in the excitement. Thank you for finding it for me." Somewhat mollified, Grace handed it to her. As she did, a card fell from it to Melissa's lap. Melissa picked it up, seeing it was one of Brandon's business cards.

On the back he had written in a square but unique script, "It was great while it lasted, Snowbird. Hope you find what you're looking for in your new life." That was all. Melissa turned ashen beneath her tan, the finality of the message cutting to her heart. She would never know the pain it had caused the tall, dark-headed man to write the chilling words when his unreasoning heart had longed to beg her forgiveness but his calculating mind had known he must not.

Tears sprang to her eyes. Ashamedly she tried wiping them away with her slim wrist.

"Here, use this." Grace offered a fresh tissue. "I've been weeping off and on myself all morning. One tends to become emotional at times like these."

I'm sure she thinks these tears are for Julia, Melissa thought, as she dried her eyes and forced herself to regain her composure. At least I hope so.

"That's better." Grace patted her arm comfortingly. "I read recently that tears are thought to have healing properties and that it can be beneficial to cry."

A few tears can't heal the open wound of anguish and heartbreak I feel this morning, Melissa thought disconsolately.

"Now, Melissa, I've been talking to Warren. Please, hear me through before you decide. If you say no, we'll understand—do please don't feel you have to agree."

Wondering what Grace was talking about, Melissa forced her mind to listen. "As I said earlier, it's going to be terribly quiet here after you and Jana leave. I don't think I could bear it. Warren and I would have to go someplace where there are people. We had planned to take the boat out, but it would be too lonely with just the two of us.

"I was thinking—and he readily agreed—that we—Warren and I, that is—could take you and Jana and Brandy up to Alaska on our boat. I know it would add another fortnight to your stay with us"—her eyes held a softly pleading look—"but I know you were worried about shipping the dog by air all that way, and if you'll let us take you there, you'll be doing us a great favor."

Melissa thought for a moment. It would be the perfect solution to her problems. She knew she'd need some time to fill the aching void left by Brandon's departure. This kind woman was offering her two weeks of respite in which to try to lick her wounds before beginning her new life.

"How kind of you to offer, Grace!" Melissa said in gratitude, rising to give her a brief hug. "How could I possibly refuse such generosity? It would be the perfect ending to the fabulous time we've spent here. I'm sure that nothing would please Jana more than to be with you both for another two weeks. Thank you."

Grace smiled happily. "I'll go tell Warren. He'll be as thrilled as I am. Do you mind if I also tell Jana?"

"Please do," Melissa answered with a weak smile.

Alone again, Melissa reread the message on the card. So cold. So final. Like the end of a shallow but intense shipboard romance.

She looked down at the bouquet on her lap through a haze of tears. Touching the waxy but wilted petals of a fantastic white orchid, she thought of how it had looked when Julia had carried it triumphantly up the aisle. Remembering how Julia had tossed it directly at her, high above the group of young women gathered around her, she knew that Julia wished her the promise of which it was a token. If only happiness could be passed from one person to another by such a simple gesture.

This bouquet had witnessed the beginning of Julia's new life in love and the ending of her own in harsh words and rejection. How different an adult love affair was from a teenage romance. Two young people could heedlessly fall in love, unencumbered by the past, with only bright hope for their future together. They had little knowledge of the world, holding to their belief in fairy tales that after they were married they would live happily ever after. . . . If only that were true!

But life isn't like that, Melissa thought realistically. Life is partially what you make it, and she had a right and an obligation to herself to become a fulfilled person. Why couldn't Brandon see that? No matter the reason, clearly he couldn't . . . or at least he didn't love her enough to try. It was better that their affair had ended now before they hurt each other more, she realized, but she found little comfort in that thought. Her heart was still heavy with melancholy.

Sighing, she stood up, squared her slender shoulders, and reluctantly joined the others on the lawn. Grace had told Jana the news of the boat trip and the child was bubbling with enthusiasm. It was difficult to remain distraught in the presence of such joyousness. Bending, Melissa buried her face in her daughter's fair fragrant hair.

CHAPTER NINE

On board the sixty-one-foot yacht, cutting through the deep swells of the Pacific, miles away from sight of land, Melissa felt almost as though no one else existed, as though no cares other than the immediate ones of keeping the boat on course and preparing meals were important, as though nothing mattered more than enjoying the companionship of Grace, Warren, Jana, and the two college boys who crewed the boat . . . almost, but not quite.

Consequently, Melissa frantically filled her time, not wanting any empty moments—taking lessons from Warren in chart and compass reading, even taking her turn at the wheel; learning from Grace how to prepare fabulous meals in spite of the limitations imposed by the small galley; playing chess with the deckhands after dinner while Warren took his watch; and in between times, reading to and playing with Jana.

It would have been an idyllic existence if her nights had been free from damnable intruding thoughts of Brandon Kade. But no matter how full her day had been, no matter how late she'd stayed up, the image of Brandon was there in her cabin waiting for her as she laid her head on the pillow, waiting impatiently to rob her night of sleep.

Diabolically, as she forcibly shut her eyes, a projector would click on in her brain playing vivid Technicolor scenes —always of Brandon: the wind ruffling his ebony black hair as he ran effortlessly along the beach; tantalizingly naked except for snug swim trunks, his white smile flashing in the sunlight. When she finally managed to blink the unbidden images away, Melissa would turn to confront him again, this time fully clothed, suavely immaculate in his tuxedo, waiting for her as she walked down a red-carpeted aisle under the shade of immense cypress trees—each scene so vital, so accurate in every heart-wrenching detail, so much a part of her, and yet, no more real then flickering images caught on a strip of celluloid.

Painful though the memories were, she secretly cherished each, not wanting time to fade their color, blur their distinction, diminish them in any way. All she had left of him were these treasured memories and the gold medallion she wore close to her heart. Regrettably, in the few short months she'd known him, Brandon Kade had become the very center of her existence: in his arms she'd scaled fabulous heights of love and passion—away from him she suffered the sharp, poignantly tormenting pain of hurt and anger. No matter where she was, no matter what she was doing, all her thoughts and feelings revolved around him.

Paradoxically she wondered, would she never be free? Why couldn't the bitter memory of their last night together wipe away all others, cancelling out the glowing happiness she'd found in his arms? Why couldn't she make herself believe the words her rational mind insistently spoke?—he doesn't love you . . . he never loved you. Why couldn't she accept the finality of their parting? Accept the frightening loneliness that gripped her heart when the gray dawn filtered through the louvered blinds, inevitably bringing the new day? Another day taking her further away from Brandon Kade.

As the climate cooled and the faultlessly blue sky took on a hazy cast, Melissa knew they were approaching the halfway mark on their trip north: Seattle. Entering familiar Puget Sound, cruising past the lushly green San Juan Islands that dotted the Strait of Juan de Fuca, Melissa realized that her turbulent thoughts about Brandon had gradually calmed. She could think of him now without her eyes misting, without the cold hand of remorse clutching her heart. She could almost make herself believe their parting had been for the best, that their affair had been a senseless infatuation —nothing more than a sizzling premature relationship based on pure sexual attraction, fanned into open flame by the romance of Scott and Julia's wedding—an infatuation doomed to burn itself out early because of their lack of mutual understanding. And even though the embers of love still smoldered, even though a fleeting memory of his face and voice brought to mind by a chance reminder could still capture and hold her spellbound in the midst of other activity, she knew she would somehow get over him.

A new life awaited her in Alaska. Yet thoughts of it seemed to enclose, bind—almost suffocate, her free spirit. But that was foolish, she told herself. She was anxious to begin practicing law, and where better to begin than in a place that was waiting for her, among people who wanted her? Her spirits lifted a little as she grasped this one comforting idea and struggled to keep it uppermost in her mind. But life without Brandon? How could that be? The bleak thought that she was destined to live out her life in one place and he in another was too painful for her to deal with. She pushed it quickly from her mind.

The beautiful distinctive skyline of Seattle appeared as they came in between Whidbey Island and the mainland. They planned to berth at Shilshole for a day of shopping—Grace needed to stock up on fresh provisions for the galley. Melissa dressed Jana quickly so that she could be off with Warren and the dogs—all were restless to be on firm ground. The judge intended to pick up any mail that had been forwarded to the marina—they all hoped for news of the newlyweds—and to obtain a rental car.

While they were gone, Melissa had time for a leisurely shower. Having become used to the casualness of boat life, she realized she'd have to take more time with her hair since she planned to spend the day in the city. It was becoming longer, growing out enough to need curling over her ears and at her nape. A few deft turns of her curling iron created a soft effect about her face. She pulled on a pastel pink culotte skirt, topped it with a matching jersey, and slipped her bare feet into canvas wedge-heeled shoes. After fastening the fine gold chains she customarily wore at her throat, she added the medallion—as she'd done every day since Brandon had first placed it around her neck.

Hearing footsteps on the deck above while she was putting on large gold hoop earrings, Melissa assumed Jana and the judge had returned. Taking one final look in the mirror, she was satisfied with the results. Noticing her high cheekbones were even more prominent than usual, she realized she must have lost a little weight. Perhaps I should have taken up modeling, she thought without vanity. Now that's a real "woman's" profession! One Brandon would have approved of! Indeed, the face and figure reflected back to her eyes could have easily graced the cover of most fashion publications in the world. It didn't occur to her that it had only been since Brandon had come into her life that she had begun to be aware of and believe in her own beauty.

Emerging topside, taking a pleasant breath of crisp morning air, Melissa was unprepared for the sight of Brandon's straight broad back. Barely able to stifle a gasp, her heart lurched at the sight of his intimately familiar male figure clad in a white windbreaker and slim white jeans. Absurdly, her fingers longed to touch the dark hair where it curled above his collar. What was he doing here? With sudden panic she wondered if something had happened to Scott and Julia.

"Mommy, look who was at the post office!" Jana cried, jumping up and down in excitement. "It's Uncle Brandon!"

"Good morning, Melissa," he said formally, with a slight inclination of his head. Frosty blue eyes slowly searched the contours of her body, clinging to the medallion, causing her knees to weaken and her heart to race within her breast. Trying for casualness, her hand reached out for a railing, searching for the support she suddenly needed.

"Hello, Brandon," she answered, her heart continuing to pound wildly. She tried to remain impassive, showing no sign of pleasure or displeasure at seeing him again, but for Jana's sake she had, at least, to be civil.

In the awkward lull when no one spoke, Brandon's eyes seemed to bore deep into her soul, bringing back to the surface all the feelings she had just lately buried there.

Grace joined them, her worried face reflecting the momentary panic Melissa had felt. Warren, noticing Grace's expression, quickly said, "Brandon has been asked to defend Dr. Todd Pearson, the heart surgeon accused of hiring his wife's killer and of orchestrating her death. After gathering as much evidence as he could, he's come to confer with me as to the plausibility of the man's innocence before he accepts or declines the case.

"It will be an intricate and drawn-out affair, and if the news media get hold of any idea that Brandon's involved, they may jeopardize the possibility of a fair trial. He's prepared a partial brief and needs to finish it. I've offered him the sanctuary of the boat and whatever help I can give for the next few days while we're on our way to Anchorage."

"Of course," Grace agreed unhesitatingly, with an audible sigh of relief. "Welcome aboard, Brandon." She reached up maternally to kiss him on the cheek. "I'm glad we have a spare cabin so you don't have to bunk in the lounge!"

Melissa experienced an unbidden sensation of regret to find that she wasn't the reason for his unheralded appearance—foolishly, for just a moment, she'd hoped that he'd come to make things right between them. But that could never be. Still, a sense of relief flooded over her at the disclosure that he was not bringing bad news about Julia and Scott. But why did he have to come now to upset her painfully recaptured equilibrium? It would be only a few more days before she would disembark and set off on her new career. There was no need to open up, even on the most superficial level, a relationship that had been closed so peremptorily by that cynical, heartbreaking note—its words still stung in her memory. *She didn't need this!*

Wondering briefly if she could beg off, Melissa decided she couldn't do so gracefully, so they went to breakfast—all five of them crowding into the compact rental car. Sitting opposite her at the table in a well-lighted family-style restaurant, Brandon ate very little. Melissa, aware of his eyes on her, did little more than pick at her food.

"Mommy, you aren't eating anything!" Jana pointed out loudly, to Melissa's acute embarrassment.

"She's right, dear," Grace said. "I've been noticing the same thing, and this morning it's worse than usual. I think you're losing weight too. Don't you think so, Brandon?"

A look of amusement flickered over his face before Brandon suggested solicitously, "Perhaps sea travel doesn't agree with you, Melissa."

"Oh, do you think that could be it?" Grace asked, concern in her voice.

"That's not it at all!" Melissa replied, her eyes smoldering with the anger she felt toward him for making the uncomfortable situation worse. "In fact, it agrees with me so well, I find it so invigorating, that I don't need as much food."

Thoroughly enjoying his pancakes and sausage, Warren remarked, "I think it's the younger generation, dear. Look at Julia. She doesn't eat enough to keep a bird alive, but she seems to thrive. That young man of hers skips lunches to work out, I know that for a fact. And Brandon here . . . I always thought he had a substantial appetite, but I must have been mistaken. He seems to have become like all the rest."

Brandon reddened as they all stared conspicuously at his plate, more than three-quarters full of its original contents.

Aha! The tables have been turned! Melissa thought, smiling innocently at his discomfiture.

Unwilling to have his eating habits the subject of their scrutiny, Brandon quickly changed the topic of conversation to what their plans were for the day. Jana coaxed and cajoled until she prevailed upon him to join her and Warren on their trip to the Seattle Aquarium. After feebly protesting that he couldn't spare the time, Brandon capitulated to the wishes of the little girl. It seemed he could deny Jana nothing, Melissa thought with amazement.

Melissa and Grace drove up the hill to the Pike Place Market after dropping the others off at the waterfront, and in an hour or two managed to fill the car with their purchases of pastries, fresh fruits, vegetables, meat, and fish. Melissa silently congratulated herself on the way she was bearing the knowledge that Brandon would be near during the rest of their trip. Grace betrayed no awareness that she and Brandon had shared more than a casual friendship as she chatted happily about the letter she had received from Julia.

The day passed quickly, ending with one last meal ashore that evening at a charming waterfront restaurant established on an old pier. They shared the house specialty, a "Pacific Northwest Seafood Feast": rich creamy clam chowder, crisp shrimp salad with garlic almond dressing, succulent butter clams in their shells, and the main course of flaky king salmon, served with warm crusty sourdough bread. Determinedly, Melissa ate her fair share and noticed with mixed feelings that Brandon did the same.

Everyone retired to their cabins as soon as they boarded, since the plan was to cast off at daybreak. Relieved that there had not been any time when she and Brandon had been alone together, Melissa thought she heard his footsteps pause briefly, then go on past her cabin and up onto the deck after everyone else had fallen asleep. Managing to resist a strong impulse to follow him, she let the gentle motion of the boat lull her to fitful sleep.

An urgent tap awakened her. "Melissa"—she heard the unmistakable voice of Brandon Kade through the slatted door—"Melissa, please come out. I need to talk with you."

Going to the door, she spoke softly through the slats so as not to awaken Jana. "Go away. I don't have anything to say to you." Her voice came out shakily, huskily. I don't, she told her wavering resolve. Nothing could come of it. He'd told her all she ever wanted to hear from him . . . and a good deal more. What more could he say? Make an apology for his brutish behavior? An apology she'd be forced to accept, pretending that they could be casual friends? So his stay on the boat could be bearable . . . for him? "Go away!" she repeated vehemently.

"Damn it, Melissa"—his deep voice hardened—"come out of there!" He rattled the knob ominously.

"Stop that," she hissed, "before you awaken the whole boat. I'm *not* coming out!"

"I'm not going away until you do."

There was no question that he meant it, she realized with a sigh, hastily slipping her arms into a robe and taking a swipe at her hair with a handy brush before quietly opening the door.

As soon as she opened the door she knew it had been a mistake. The sight of his massive figure seemed overwhelming, almost completely filling the frame. When he reached forward to take her arm, she yanked it away and preceded him up to the lounge, where a shell-shaped night-light glowed against the teak wall. Turning her to face him, he took her in his arms, pressing her slight body against the familiar hard planes of his, instantly sparking a fire that seared through her like a bolt of lightning. As his lips came down to claim hers, she turned her head with the last vestige of strength her weakening body held, so that his mouth met the tender flesh of her neck, sending a shiver rippling through her arching body, as an involuntary moan escaped her constricted throat.

"Don't touch me, Brandon," she commanded in cold fury. But he heedlessly opened her robe, pushing aside the plunging neckline of her sheer gown, exposing her rounded breasts tipped by aroused pink buds. He gasped, shudderingly, as his hands caressed their creamy perfection, his thumbs and forefingers stroking their hardened tips. Melissa lay helpless in his arms, her pulse pounding deafeningly, beating stirringly in her inner recesses, sparking an urgent warmth in her veins. Bending his head, he reverently, longingly kissed each throbbing globe with lips warm and moist, sending a burning, fierce excitement to cruelly tantalize her now undeniable desire for him.

"I can't let you go," he whispered huskily against her flesh. "I'll *never* let you go! This past week has been hell without you. I thought I could get my life together once you were out of it, but I haven't been able to eat, drink, or sleep . . ." His voice faded to a low groan of desire. Loosening her robe tie, while holding her closely to his chest, he slipped her supple arms from it. She made no effort to resist—her body helplessly captive to the sensuous flow of ecstasy that swept her resolve away, melted her defenses like sand castles succumbing to the relentless tide.

Enflamed, she reacted to his scorching urgency, responded fully to the seduction of his passion, her lips clinging hungrily to his as he eased her gown over her shoulders. His large hands followed its descent over each delineated rib, in at the narrowed waist, down over rounded feminine hips; shiver after shiver of delirious delight followed his touch. The intensity of her own desire met his as she freed his body and they sank together to the carpeted floor.

In an instant his vibrant masculinity was within her, touching off an explosion of sheer physical joy. Through the roaring in her ears she heard his voice in ragged fragments, "Be mine, Melissa. Marry me." Unable to answer with her womanly flesh in total control of her will, she met his strong thrust with welcoming writhing beats of her own hips, until at last she was drawn to the peak of rapture with the flooding release of liquid velvet within her.

Lying cradled against his fulfilled length, Melissa slowly came to her senses. Good lord! They were on the floor of the lounge, in full view of anyone who might wander in in search of a cup of coffee. Thank God, they were still berthed at the marina, or someone surely would have witnessed their wanton act from the bridge! Grabbing her robe, she struggled to her feet, hastily jabbing her arms into its sleeves. In the same moment Brandon was on his feet and wrapped in his robe.

He caught her as she turned to run. "Melissa, don't go, I love you. I want you to be my wife. I was wrong to leave you in La Jolla, but you were so adamant about our differences I thought we'd be better breaking it off before we went any further. But now I know you love me, and that's all that counts. Give up your ideas about being tied to Alaska and your father-in-law. Leave with me when I fly out from Anchorage. We'll be married right away and I'll spend the rest of my life making you happy. You won't regret it, I promise you that. I'll give you anything you ever want. I'll take you with me everywhere I go. We'll never be separated."

Dizzily, giddily Melissa looked up into his darkly handsome face, the face she loved so much, as though to memorize every line and feature of it. She heard his words, and with a chilling heart understood their meaning—he offered her his life as long as she would go where he went—as long as she would do what he asked. She shook her head slightly in disbelief. How could he misunderstand her so thoroughly? Why couldn't he see that she was a person in her own right? That what she needed was a life with a strand running parallel to his—a life of her own design and plan, that touched and was bonded to his with mutual love and support?

Clearly he couldn't. There was no room for her personal growth or individuality in the type of marriage he offered. Always at his beck and call, she would be no more than a subordinate being.

"No, Brandon, no," she heard her voice saying as if from a great hollow distance. "Don't say any more. That's not the kind of life I want for myself and my daughter. I won't be a satellite revolving around your star."

Glinting anger warred with disappointment in his stormy blue eyes. "I came here to offer you myself, and if that isn't enough I don't know what more you want!"

She pulled her hands from his grip. "It's no use trying to explain further—you'd never understand. My needs and obligations are meaningless because they don't all center around you. They don't fit into your plans!" Tears stinging behind her eyelids, she didn't trust herself to speak further—anything she could say would only add to the hurt . . . for both of them.

He didn't move to stop her as she slowly descended the steps to her stateroom. Now it was really finished. As limp as a rag doll, she could barely turn the handle to her room. She entered the cabin and stood leaning against the door for support; she stood a long time allowing her reeling mind to clear enough to function.

Dropping down onto her bed, she began to pound the downy pillow. She'd wipe him from her thoughts. She wouldn't think of him again. "I hate him! I hate him! I hate him!" she whispered under her breath, thinking how insufferably didactic he was . . . and how desperately unhappy she was at having to turn her back on what she knew with dreadful certainty would prove to be the great love of her life.

Brandon stayed on deck, leaning on the fog-dampened rail far into the cold night, locked in argument with himself. What the hell was he doing here anyway? It was just as he'd known it would be that last night in La Jolla. Well, it was obvious Melissa wasn't in love with him. Oh, she wanted him all right, wanted him as much as he wanted her, but clearly not enough to change her life for him. She'd turned him down flat! Refused to marry him. Told him he'd never understand her! At least she was right about that; he twisted his lips in a grim parody of a smile. Well, he'd be damned if he ever fell for another woman. What would marriage to someone like her be, anyhow, but a tether tying him down! He'd managed fine without love for thirty-eight years and he'd do it again once he got her out of his life. He'd jump ship and head for home right now if that were possible.

Slumping glumly into a deck chair he tried to forget how soft and sweetly pliant her womanly body, which he'd held for the last time, was—how responsive and giving her mouth, which he'd kissed for the last time, could be. He let out a groan of anguish; one fist crashed resoundingly on the wooden arm of the chair while his other hand covered his stricken face.

The days passed fitfully, Melissa's nerves constantly on edge. While Brandon conferred with the judge in the boat's lounge, the contents of his briefcase spread out around them on the game table, Melissa did her best to keep Jana occupied and out of their way. Though curious to know the particulars of the case on which he was working and keen to observe the manner in which he approached it, she wouldn't have considered questioning him about it. Bitterly she realized he refused to think of her as a fellow lawyer. He was civilly cool whenever she was near, and though the very sight of him aroused memories too disturbing for her mind to hold, she hoped she appeared just as unaffected as he.

And yet, there were times she would feel his eyes upon her and would turn to see a hurt on his face that would wrench her heart. Their eyes would hold for a long moment before he'd divert his gaze. Ridiculously, she'd have to stifle the impulse of her wayward body to run to him, hold him and kiss the hurt away. At other times she would seethe with fury at him for having invaded the time she had taken to dispel him from her mind—for having imposed himself on a trip that was to be used for getting over him. Loneliness gripped her heart—a loneliness that she knew would be hers until he was out of her life. But how could she even hope to get over him when he was there in the close confines of the yacht? His deep voice audible throughout the boat; his face ever before her at mealtimes; the scent of his after-shave eddying through the corridors and slats of the stateroom doors; the sound of his distinctively proud footsteps moving about.

How could he be so callous? How could he sit there engrossed in work when her heart literally screamed with pain? She counted the slow hours of anguish as they passed. Soon Brandon Kade would be only a memory, a memory that would fade in time—she hoped.

The only tie between them was Jana, and Melissa was grateful he treated her as always, playfully and lovingly. She couldn't stand to think of her daughter suffering as she was because of him. Though she avoided him whenever possible, shared meals were inescapable. Food had lost its taste, she had difficulty swallowing, and at times the very nearness of him would cause her hand to tremble so violently she was afraid to raise her cup to her lips. Only Grace's sympathetic glances at these telling moments helped Melissa keep her composure.

One afternoon when they were alone on deck, Grace remarked, "I don't want to pry into anything that isn't my business, dear, but I've become very fond of you. Actually, all summer I was aware that you and Brandon were growing close, but I can't help but see that something's wrong between the two of you. Is there anything I can do to help?" A frown of concern furrowed her usually placid forehead.

"There isn't anything anyone can do. I appreciate your

caring, but don't worry, I'll make it. There are only two more days left," Melissa assured her. "I'm sorry to cause you any worry after the marvelous time you and Warren have given Jana and me. Thanks, anyway."

"Well, whatever the problem is," Grace said, looking significantly toward the lounge, "I know it must be Brandon's fault. He can be so exasperatingly obstinate. But don't give up on him, Melissa, he needs you. You bring out the best in him."

In a chill mist of fog and light rain they reached Homer, a picturesque fishing village sheltered on a bay at the opening of Cook Inlet, less than a hundred miles from Anchorage. Melissa was flooded with memories of midsummer nights when she'd come there with Laurence and Sonny to share the holiday atmosphere of the small town, sitting on the pier far into the twilit night watching the golden red sun dip toward the horizon, then rise again without ever setting. An unusual feeling of homesickness swept over her, and although Laurence and Irene expected her home the following day, she felt the urge to call them and talk with them. But when Warren tried to make radiophone contact with the mainland, the atmospheric disturbance of the far north was too great to get anything but static.

Warren offered to take her to shore in the eighteen-foot lifeboat, but Brandon interjected, "I'll do it. I need to check in with my secretary and to confirm my plane reservations."

"Wonderful!" Grace enthusiastically exclaimed. "Be sure to dress warmly, Melissa. It's quite cold tonight. There's an orange flotation windbreaker in your cabin. And Brandon, you be sure to wear yours too. Warren, have the boys lower the Boston Whaler," she added unnecessarily, in an effort to fill the void left by Melissa's obvious lack of response.

"Can I come too?" Jana asked, pulling on her mother's hand.

"May I," Melissa automatically corrected.

"No, dear," Grace answered quickly, putting her arm around the child's shoulders, pulling her close. "I think two wet people will be quite enough. Besides I've noticed you sniffling a bit today and don't want to put you on shore tomorrow with a cold. You and I will curl up with your favorite books and spend this last evening together. I'm going to miss you very much." She smiled winningly into the little girl's upturned face.

So it was settled before Melissa could think of or act upon any objections she might have. Why not? she asked herself. What could happen between her and Brandon in Homer, let alone in a dinghy on a choppy sea?

In spite of Grace's cautionary warnings and a wealth of heavy clothing, Melissa was frozen by the time they docked. She and Brandon made for the shelter of the closest tavern, where they found a phone booth.

"Let's have a drink first," Brandon suggested, leading her to a booth at the back of the warm noisy room, unzipping his jacket as he went. Melissa's stiffened fingers fumbled at the zipper of hers, causing it to catch on the side material. "Here, let me help you with that," he offered.

The accidental touch of his hand brushing her neck as she raised her chin high above the collar—the nearness of his face as he peered closely at the stubborn zipper—the mingling of their breath as he pried the material away from the metal slide—caused an intimate tension between them, making his adept fingers uncustomarily clumsy, and causing her heart to pound ridiculously, erratically in her breast.

The man was a hazard—hazardous to her health and well-being. More than hazardous—downright dangerous. The sooner she got the call over with and was back on the boat, the sooner she could relax. The longer she stood near him, the more foolishly her body reacted, until her breath was coming out in short uncontrollable pants, her lungs full and affected by the fresh, slightly scented aroma of him, intoxicating and warming her as no amount of alcohol could ever do. Her cold fingers tingled, her throat burned where he'd touched her, and her pounding heart sent heated blood to beat at her temples. After what seemed an eternity, the catch came free in a sudden plunge that opened her jacket completely, sending his hand down over her breasts to a momentary resting point on her abdomen, where a pulse throbbed deeply. Jumping back as though burned, she sat down heavily on the wooden bench.

Brandon hesitated a moment, as though deciding whether to sit next to her or across the table. Melissa was grateful when he chose the opposite bench. "What'll it be?" he asked huskily. Clearly he'd been as shaken as she by the unexpected physical contact.

"Whatever you're having," she managed. "While you order I'll make my call." Cold and tension stiffened her legs, but she was glad of the chance to do anything to get away from his disturbing presence.

Returning to the table after a short conversation with her father-in-law, she fought down the impulse to shrink as far back in the corner of the booth as she could—to put as much distance as possible between Brandon and her yearning body.

"Did you get through all right?" he asked, raising a glass of white wine to his lips.

"Yes, they'll be down at the marina to meet us," she answered, busying her hands with the heavy goblet and the paper coaster beneath it.

"I'm anxious to meet the man I've almost come to think of as my rival," Brandon said gruffly, his mouth pulled in a sardonic half smile.

"Oh, Brandon. That's ridiculous. Let's not start that again," she begged, her eyes meeting his imploringly. And then, as their eyes held, a wave of realization that this was truly the last they'd see of each other swept over her, and sadness constricted her throat.

"Then again, maybe I'd rather not meet him. I'll make my

calls now," he said tersely, rising from the table. "Order me a double scotch on the rocks."

Melissa blinked back the searing tears that threatened to course down her cheeks. Sipping her wine, she determined to get herself under control, forced herself to remember her firm decision to get over loving this man. But the pain in her heart was sickening, a raw, gnawing torment. She put on her stiff jacket while he was gone, fearing the contact an offer of help would bring. Returning, Brandon sat just long enough to take a couple of deep swallows from the fresh drink that had been placed before him, signal the waiter, lay a bill on the table, and motion to Melissa that it was time to leave.

Darkness enveloped them when they came out into the silence of the evening . . . a silence that echoed their own. They found the boat covered with a film of dampness; after rummaging in a small forward compartment, Brandon pulled out a dry flotation pillow for Melissa to sit on. Standing in the middle of the boat at the upright wheel and console controls, he started the engine and made for the dim lights of the anchored yacht, now shrouded in fog.

Melissa wished she were not so conscious of the muscular power in his lean hard body, wished she could keep her eyes from the broadness of his shoulders and the trimness of his hips above his long masculinely shapely legs encased in slim jeans. The very maleness of him aroused her femininity, tugged provocatively at her senses. The short trip seemed endless, unbearable. It had been a terrible mistake to think that she could ever be alone with him without that crazy chemistry erupting between them creating an elixir more potent and alluring than either could deny. She longed to be safe aboard the yacht, away from him—away from the mounting tightwire tension that virtually crackled in the dampness of the night.

As soon as the Whaler reached the yacht, Brandon began fastening the rope through the fittings. Melissa hurried forward toward the boarding ladder, brushing aside his helping hand. Catching him off guard, her action toppled him off balance. He put back a foot to steady himself, tipping the craft sideways, throwing Melissa against his chest with enough force that they both went down on the floor in a tumbled heap—the rope sliding loose from the ring, the dinghy floating free, away from the boat.

The arms that held her were steel bands, the fingers that threaded themselves through her hair forced her head back, the mouth that came down upon hers commanded her body to comply to the sensual demands of his. She struggled against his powerful strength, desperately trying to free herself from his passionate hold, but the body that struggled against his truly wanted nothing more than to feel his length against it, wanted nothing more than to be full of him, savoring every promise he offered. Her lips thirsted for his, her arms longed to encircle the muscular column of his neck, her abdomen yearned to feel the thrust of his arousal once more before he would leave her forever. When he roughly tossed her jacket aside and his hand found the warm breasts beneath her sweater, she opened her lips to receive his thrusting tongue, meeting it in a duel of reciprocating pleasure. She wanted him, wanted him desperately this one last time. She wanted to somehow show him, convince him that she cared for him, loved him in a fathomless eternal way that transcended the irreconcilable differences that would forever keep them apart.

Mindless of the cold drizzle and the floating dinghy, completely unconscious of the dangerous rocky pitching of the small craft in the northern sea, they made rapturous love—half clothed, heedless of the cramped uncomfortable position that red scuffs and blue bruises would later attest to. She held him to her in a frenzy of possession, knowing that all too soon the dawn would come and he would leave her—leave her with only this one last intimate bond between them—this crazy, tilting, whirling, yet somehow wholly satisfying union of their loving bodies. She never wanted this memory to fade—it would be hers, she thought in an instant of transported bliss as they reached fulfillment together. Peculiarly, the act had a healing, almost soothing effect, drawing their spirits close. Laughingly they helped each other straighten, button, and zip their clothing with a sense of rightness and closeness that was odd considering their imminent estrangement.

"If the Boston Whaler people want a unique testimonial to the worthiness of their vessel, I think we could give them something special—a little out of the ordinary," Brandon joked as he smoothed his hair. "But the next time we make love I hope to hell it'll be on a bed—a king size one at that."

Suddenly Melissa felt the chill of the night—felt the clammy dampness of her clothing, felt a creeping numbness replacing the thrill of their passion. "There won't be a next time." The bitter knowledge twisted and turned inside her, piercing her heart with remembered sharp, cold reality. She felt guilty, selfish, as though she'd used him, maneuvered him for one last precious memory.

"How can you say that!" he demanded, grasping her slight shoulders with his powerful hands, as though by doing so his will would transmit itself to her. "You love me. I know you do. Say it, damn it, say it!" He lightly shook her, his face angrily thrust close to hers.

"Yes, Brandon," she breathed, her eyes shut tightly against his enraged yet endearing face. "I love you, and I wish to God I didn't!" Her voice weighted with wretchedness, she covered her face with trembling hands, sinking to the seat, sliding through the hands that no longer gripped her.

He kneeled on one knee beside her, his large hands now stroking her arms, "Melissa, I'm going to ask you one last time. Will you marry me—now?"

Letting her hands drop, she gently took his face between them, "Brandon, I can't. You knew that before tonight happened. You haven't changed. Nothing's changed."

Abruptly he stood, and when he spoke, his words were almost frightening in their controlled absolute lack of emotion. "You're right, nothing's changed. I can sure as hell see that now, and it never will."

It was a taut, resolute Melissa who walked down the pier with the Raymonds to where Laurence Bennett was waiting. Jana, with Brandy on a leash, ran on ahead to greet her grandfather, who gathered her up in a fond bear hug.

Melissa didn't know whether Brandon was watching or not. He'd chosen to busy himself in his cabin preparing for his departure rather than to meet the man he considered a rival for her affections. No matter—he would never know how difficult it was for her to take each step that led away from him. He would never know how she felt the intimate bond between them stretch and pull unendurably on her resolve—tearing at the love she still felt for him, would always feel for him.

Their farewells after an early breakfast had been succinct, although Brandon had been affectionate and demonstrative with Jana, even promising to see her again, if and when his business took him to Alaska. When Jana promised to teach him to cross-country ski, as he'd taught her tennis, he told her he'd take her up on that someday. A final hug and a pat on the dog's head had sent her on her way. Melissa was glad to have it over and done with. She couldn't bear to see them together.

It was difficult to say good-bye to the Raymonds. At their insistence Melissa promised that she and Jana would come to stay with them again. Jana's childishly extravagant remark announcing that she would rather visit them than go anywhere else in the world clearly pleased them.

When Laurence cordially offered them the hospitality of his home, Warren declined with thanks, explaining that his time was limited and he was anxious to be off to explore the Columbia Glacier area and back down the inside passage where he and Grace intended to take the fabulous sidetrips they'd bypassed on their way up the coast.

The moment of parting was painful, with teary hugs all around. Melissa was touched to see the judge surreptitiously wiping a stray tear or two from his eyes as he kissed Jana a final farewell. Remembering the small compact of pills Julia had carelessly tossed her that evening in La Jolla, Melissa knew her friend had made the right decision in deciding to have a child right away. The generous Raymonds needed to see their family circle expanded.

A little over an hour after they'd moored, a somber-faced Brandon Kade boarded a Wien Air Alaska flight for Seattle with connections to San Francisco. After ordering a dry martini, he stared moodily out of the window of his first-class cabin seat, seeing not the clouds surrounding the plane but Melissa's blondly beautiful face.

"Damn that woman!" he forcibly said aloud, startling the clergyman who was his seatmate to wakefulness.

CHAPTER TEN

The Bennett residence, its many sprawling rooms built on the bedrock of the Chugach foothills, never failed to remind Melissa of the stolid man who had built it. The simple yet contemporary lines of the sturdy stone structure, well buttressed to withstand the elements, reflected the forthright mind and personality of Laurence Bennett, Sr., personifying the rugged yet dignified role he played in civic leadership, though a relative newcomer to the frontier community. With the rightness of its position following the contours of the land, nestled among the natural landscaping of its grounds, it projected an aura of having been there forever—just as Laurence successfully projected the image of a founding father.

Its commanding aspect before its own private mountain lake, which moored the typical seaplane no affluent Anchorage resident would be without, attested to his prestige, gained through sponsoring or heading many civic financial activities and charities. Melissa smiled, thinking of his tall lean figure, with his lined yet handsome deeply tanned face, at the center of the public and social gatherings he loved so well. She knew that he enjoyed holding court at his private club among respectful peers who readily acknowledged his shrewd community leadership and business acumen.

Happy to be back in the only home she had ever known, Jana endlessly shared memories of her vacation with her beloved nana. Irene, a kindly woman whose Scandinavian heritage was apparent in her abundant gray-streaked blond hair and the fine features of her expressive face, would give her undivided attention to the photographs Jana would spread out all over the table in the country kitchen. She'd smile indulgently when Jana would tire of her tales and jump up to take Brandy for a run along the lakeshore. In the days that followed their homecoming Melissa grew to admire Irene more and more.

One morning as she and Irene sat lingering over their breakfast coffee, Melissa reached out, giving the older woman's hand a squeeze. "I want to thank you for taking care of Jana for me. Knowing she had your loving care was the only thing that made these past three years bearable. I must admit, though, at times I was a little jealous of your closeness and her dependency on you."

Irene smiled, giving a warm laugh. "Well, I have to admit your feelings weren't entirely groundless. After we left you two in Seattle, I was uneasy," she confessed. "Jana had been almost my baby for quite a while, as you know, and it was difficult to give her up. It was an adjustment for me but one I realized I had to make. I'm glad you're both home now though."

Irene's face sobered, and she hesitated a moment before continuing. "Frankly, I had some other reservations about your return. I was afraid that once you were back, you'd want to run the house again and that my presence here would become unnecessary."

"Oh, Irene, that's the furthest thing from my intention." Melissa shook her blond head in sincere disbelief. "I didn't go to law school for three years to settle down to run this house. Besides, Dad couldn't do without you. I've never seen him so contented and well taken care of in all the time I've known him.

"And look at this house"—she expansively waved an arm, indicating the charmingly decorated kitchen—"it's beautiful! I know you've done it all. Even though Dad chose quality things, it never really hung together before. The whole house is brighter and cozier now. But that's only one of the things you've accomplished that I could mention. You're indispensable."

"That's very kind of you to say," Irene sighed. "But it's about all I'm prepared to do, I'm afraid. I was widowed a few years ago. My husband and I had a very happy marriage. Unfortunately we never had children. Left with a lot of debts and no money to pay them with, I was desperate. The only thing I knew how to do was housekeeping so I decided to look for domestic work.

"Fortunately Mr. Bennett hired me to take care of Jana, and the two of them have been my whole life ever since. In my case it's all worked out well, but my advice to young women nowadays would be to follow in your footsteps. I admire you, Melissa. Everyone needs to be prepared to take care of herself if the need arises."

"Thank you, Irene. I really appreciate your saying that." Melissa wondered how much Laurence's gradually softening attitude toward her desire for a career in law had been due to this astute woman's gentle influence. Clearly she'd had an unknown ally in Irene from the start.

"But enough of my philosophizing," Irene said, as she poured them each another cup of coffee. "Let's go back to your plans. When do you think you'll begin using that office with your name on the door? Or might there be a little something else on your mind? Something that includes an extremely handsome man Jana calls Uncle Brandon?" Her hazel eyes twinkled teasingly. "He's in so many of Jana's photos with you. She's obviously become very attached to him."

Noticing the stricken look that came over Melissa's face at the mention of Brandon's name, Irene reached out to cover her hand in affection and apology. "What's the matter, dear? Please forgive me if I've said the wrong thing."

"There's nothing to forgive." Melissa smiled weakly as tears threatened. Resolutely blinking them back, steadily looking at Irene, she said, "I suppose it's best to have the subject of Brandon out in the open between us. I may need your help explaining the way things are to Jana. You're right. He and Jana are very fond of each other. And he and I"—she sighed deeply—"well . . . there are insurmountable problems between us. It looks like that office with my name on the door is my only option for the future."

Irene's eyes filled with sympathy and concern. "There are lots more fish in the sea, as my mother always said," she offered lamely. "But that's not even a consideration right now, is it, dear?" Her words were more a statement of understanding than a question.

Melissa shook her head mutely, not trusting herself to reply.

"Don't be so sure it's over, Melissa," Irene offered consolingly. "I think love for you shows in his eyes even in those pictures."

But Melissa knew what Irene could never know—that it was unlikely she would ever see Brandon Kade again. That bridge had been burned—had gone down in flames so totally consuming that not a single timber remained to span the chasm that stretched between them.

Later, in the covered heated pool behind the house, Jana and Melissa tried to recapture the fun they'd had in the Raymonds' pool, but without an appreciative audience or convivial companions they became subdued and pensive, each thinking her own thoughts.

As Melissa towed Jana quietly across the pool, Jana exclaimed, "I miss Uncle Brandon! Do you think he'll come and stay with us sometime? He promised he'd let me teach him to ski."

Melissa could only answer "Maybe," knowing in her

heart that she wanted the same, but also acknowledging to herself that "Maybe not" would be a truer answer.

Brightly changing the subject, she added, "Speaking of teaching—it's time to enroll you in school, young lady. I can't believe you're old enough for kindergarten!" She gently smoothed back her daughter's hair. "We've had our summer's fun, and now we both have to get to work."

That noon when Laurence came home for lunch, Melissa came down dressed in a smart new business suit. "I'd like to meet you downtown this afternoon, Dad," she announced at the table. "I'm anxious to see my new office. Irene tells me I even have a view."

"We're ready anytime you are. I just thought you might like a little more time for yourself," he answered, looking up from a steaming bowl of soup.

"I've had enough time off. I'm ready to get to work."

"How does two thirty sound?" Laurence asked with a wide grin.

"Perfect." Melissa smiled in return. "I'll stop by the Montessori school on the way and pick up the enrollment forms and make a registration appointment for Jana."

Melissa took the elevator directly to the ninth floor, which housed the board members' offices and Laurence Bennett's suite, bypassing the offices of the Martin, Martin and Taylor law firm located on the eighth floor of the Bennett Building in downtown Anchorage.

During Melissa's lifetime Anchorage had grown from a small town to a huge, thriving city. Bennett Enterprises, at first specializing in construction and now widely diversified in its holdings, had grown with it. Stepping out onto rich carpet, she remembered she'd often heard it said that Laurence Bennett with his sawmills in Juneau had been the right man in the right place at the right time.

Melissa greeted the receptionist and followed her into the large, imposing private office. Coming from behind his enormous mahogany desk, Laurence crossed the room to put his arm around her in a welcoming hug.

He took her down one floor to meet Ross Martin, the senior partner, who officially welcomed her into the law firm.

"Come on," Laurence urged, "enough time spent on formalities. I want you to see your office." Leading her down a wide corridor, he threw open a door.

Touched, Melissa could see an obvious effort to please her reflected in the furnishings: the color scheme in shades of green and blue; lovely light-oak furniture with brass trimmings set among green plants flourishing in the light from one entire wall of windows; another wall covered with a striking handpainted mural of a downhill racer signed by one of Alaska's most prominent artists. Several floor-to-ceiling bookcases stood empty awaiting her personal library of law texts.

"Dad, this is too much!" Melissa protested. "You didn't have to do all this. I would have been pleased with a cubicle as long as it had a desk and a filing cabinet."

"Nothing's too much for my girl." Laurence cleared his throat. "Well, now, sit down at your desk," he commanded gruffly. "I want to see how you look behind it!"

She obeyed self-consciously. She wanted to give him the pleasure of his gift, even though a little overwhelmed by his largess. "Thank you, Dad." Her smile widened as she tipped back in the blue-upholstered swivel chair. "I love it. I couldn't have done a better job if I'd picked it all out myself. You've thought of everything!" She rose and hugged him in true appreciation.

"I've been waiting a long time for another Bennett to join the firm," he whispered.

Then, turning, he announced loudly, his arm still around Melissa, "Come on, Ross, I'll buy you two a drink to celebrate." He clapped his hand on the other man's shoulder. "We'll go up to the club. I guess you'll be the first woman member, Melissa. That ought to shake 'em up some." He chuckled, and the two men exchanged amused looks.

The rest of the afternoon she toured the remainder of the Bennett Building with Laurence, meeting the heads of the divisions of the business that were quartered there. As she left the underground parking garage and moved into the slow flow of late afternoon traffic, Melissa realized she'd gone several hours without thinking of Brandon, but then his face came back into her thoughts, creating a well of emptiness that drained away the excitement of the past few hours. Maybe, when I really get down to work, I'll be able to get over him, she tried to tell herself.

The next day she and Jana visited the progressive school she'd chosen because it offered the all-day kindergarten her precocious little daughter needed. Impressed with the physical surroundings and pleased with the type of program that the charming director described to her, she was sure Jana would be happy and challenged in the pleasant environment.

She also activated her membership at the tennis club and reserved a court on a daily basis for the hour immediately following Jana's dismissal from school so that she and her daughter could have a regular fun-filled time together.

With Jana happily occupied, Melissa began her study of the Bennett Enterprises in earnest. During this period of internship, waiting to be admitted to the bar, she started within the building itself going from floor to floor getting to know the various individuals and the responsibilities involved with their positions. As she became aware of the diversity and monetary worth of the company and the intricate wells of interests held by outside investors, she could understand the need for her father-in-law, as one of the principal stock-holders and chairman of the board, to employ numerous attorneys to handle the legal aspects of the business. Perhaps, she thought, I can be happy here. Maybe I can accomplish something worthwhile in corporate law.

It was true that while she worked during the day she

became so engrossed in what she was learning that thoughts of Brandon were pushed from her mind. But nothing occupied her mind at night except memories and images of him; they seemed indelibly etched on her soul. The knowledge that he was gone—gone forever from her life—banished by her own determination that they could never be more than strangers who had once shared a brief but torrid affair, haunted her dreams.

Especially painful for her and delightful for Jana was the day a new shipment of photographs of the wedding and the boat trip to Alaska arrived from Warren. Ecstatic, trying to look at all of them at once, Jana refused to have them mounted out of sight in albums.

"Let's put them on bulletin boards and hang them in your room," Melissa suggested.

"Oh, yes," Jana agreed. "They're all mixed up now. You have to help me put them in the right order."

So for several evenings Melissa was torn in agonizing bits reliving the days on the Raymond estate and yacht. Yet somehow she welcomed the torture, wanting to remember each moment she'd been alive in Brandon's arms.

She saved for herself one especially fine close-up of Brandon seated beside the pool unaware that he was being photographed. His face, usually guarded and inscrutable, showed a moment of pleasure lighting up his eyes and softening the firm lines of his mouth. She wondered what he'd been looking at that had caused his face to show this open, vulnerable, almost worshipful gaze. What no one else could know was that it came closest to capturing his features as they looked during the times when his face was bent toward hers in love.

In the privacy of her room she took the cherished photo out to look at it again and again as waves of remembered passion pulsed through her body. Perhaps it was as well she would never know she had been the object of his attention when the photograph had been snapped . . . the knowledge would have only increased her pain.

Why did it have to be this way? Why had he forced her to make this agonizing choice? she wondered. Why hadn't he been willing to give her the time she needed to work things out? How different these days and nights would be if she knew he would be calling, if she knew he would be writing, if she knew he were planning to see her again—if she knew that someday he would be there, waiting to take her in his arms.

Lifting the picture to her cheek and holding it there while a flurry of memories deluged her mind, she wondered how long this agony would possess her before it began to fade and she could go on living without these lonely hours of excruciating hunger for him torturing her soul. She began to seriously question her wisdom in making the choice she'd made on the Raymonds' yacht.

She started accepting invitations to lunch and dinner from colleagues at the office, hoping to fill her time and keep her mind occupied beyond her business day. Her hours at the tennis club were enjoyable for the exercise her body needed and for the sheer exhaustion they produced, giving her some release in sleep.

It wasn't long before Darryl Jeffreys, who had been her lawyer after Sonny's death, asked her to be his partner in a doubles tournament. Tall, blond, fine-featured, and gregarious, thirty-five years old, he was in many ways Brandon's opposite. Politically oriented, he had used his law career as a stepping stone to become the district attorney. Popular among all classes of people, he inspired confidence with his clean-cut boyish good looks. He was clearly on the rise, and Melissa had heard the prediction more than once that someday he would be governor.

A protégé of the law firm Martin, Martin and Taylor before his election to his present position, Darryl socialized freely with the other attorneys of the firm, and Melissa frequently found herself coupled with him at social gatherings as well as at the tennis club. At first she was reluctant to spend so much time with one man, but since Darryl didn't seem to want any more from her than her company, she began to relax and even enjoy the easy camaraderie that developed between them.

In a short time dinner dates with other couples on the nights of their tennis competitions became an accepted fact. Gradually they settled into a regular routine of Friday movie dates, and whenever Darryl had tickets for a sporting event he'd call Melissa. Anchorage residents seeing them deep in conversation at a secluded table for two at the Crow's Nest or Josephine's would smile knowingly, never suspecting that the two were actually engaged in shoptalk. Melissa, an active questioning participant, enjoyed discussing Darryl's work with him, and he provided helpful tips concerning her firm.

As the weeks went on, Darryl's casual attentions gradually changed. When he was taking her home from the party celebrating her passing of the bar exams, he parked the car at the beginning of the circular drive and turned toward her.

"I had a wonderful time with you tonight, Melissa." His words came out slowly, as though chosen with care; his eyes alone communicated his unspoken desire.

"I enjoyed the party too," she hedged, realizing his feelings had reached the stage she'd hoped could be avoided. Although she admired Darryl for his rare and admirable traits, at no time had she experienced anything that could be labeled sexual attraction for him. *I should never have let it go this far,* she chastised herself. *In my need for companionship I've ignored all the signs of his growing attachment to me.*

"It was more than just the party. I couldn't keep my eyes off you all night. You're so accomplished, Counselor," he teased. "So friendly, self-assured—and what a great sense of humor. And all of it wrapped up in that gorgeous package." His eyes gleamed with admiration for her. "I'm afraid I've fallen head over heels for you. As far as I'm concerned, no other woman in Anchorage is in your league."

"But Darryl—" she protested.

"No buts about it." His arm came around her, gently pulling her close. "To be truthful, I've been crazy about you for years. I've only been waiting for you to come home to stay. Every time I'd run into your father-in-law while you were in Seattle, I'd manage to bring the conversation around to you," he said with an open grin, causing her heart to sink. "I kept praying my luck would hold—that you wouldn't fall for someone else." His finger traced the fine line of her profile.

"I was too busy for anything like that," Melissa laughed nervously, wondering how she was going to get out of kissing him without hurting his feelings. But his face drew nearer until she could see each blond eyelash surrounding his clear blue eyes. Then his lips were on hers, a firm pleasant pressure and nothing more—no sparks, no exploding fireworks—no falling stars . . . nothing.

What's the matter with me? Melissa wondered frantically. Darryl Jeffreys, the most eligible bachelor in town, is kissing me and I feel nothing. Deliberately she circled her arms around his neck, opened her lips and kissed him long and thoroughly. When they drew apart she saw that he was visibly shaken, but her pulse remained steady.

Damn you, Brandon Kade! she fumed. What have you done to me? Is this the way it's going to be the rest of my life? Have you spoiled me for other men? Venturing a glance at Darryl, she noticed with relief that he seemed satisfied.

Moving to start the motor, he remarked, "It's getting late."

At the door he bent to hold her, brushing her lips with a light kiss. "Good night, sweetheart. I'll see you tomorrow." Then he added perceptively, "Don't worry, Melissa. I'm not going to move in too fast. I'll give you all the time and space you need. I've waited this long—a little longer won't matter. I want you to be as sure about me as I am about you."

So he hadn't been fooled, she thought, slowly climbing the

polished stairs to her bedroom. Well, she decided, she would take her time and give him a chance. After all, not everyone was crazy in love with the person they married. Love often came later as two people grew close in their relationship.

She could do a lot worse than Darryl Jeffreys, she told herself, mentally ticking off his assets. He had a promising career, was kind and companionable, and quite good-looking. As she thought over their many discussions, she felt sure he would encourage her to pursue her own career. Laurence was fond of him, and he would make a fine father for Jana.

Jana might take a little convincing, Melissa thought with a grin, remembering the insightful comment the child had made after one of Darryl's visits: "He's nice, but I like Uncle Brandon more, because Darryl likes everybody just the same. Uncle Brandon really likes *me* best." In her childish wisdom she'd put her finger on the essence of Darryl's charm, Melissa knew, but she felt sure in time Darryl could win her daughter over.

Still, Brandon was a hard act to follow. And with all his assets, Darryl had one enormous liability: she didn't love him—could never love him—as she loved Brandon Kade.

As Melissa tried to sleep that night, Darryl's blond good looks and pleasing attributes couldn't dispel memories of the darkly handsome chiseled features of the face she loved.

A few evenings later over dinner, Darryl remarked, "I see Kade is on the front pages again. It's going to be interesting to see just how he gets Dr. Pearson off. One thing's for sure, that guy knows how to pick the cases that will bring the most publicity."

Melissa's temper flared, surprising Darryl, who had never seen her angry or upset. "I think he takes cases no one else will touch when he's sure justice might not be served otherwise."

Darryl laughed. "Personally, I suspect he takes cases where the clients can pay monumental fees to see that they don't end up behind bars—or if so, only for a very short period of time."

"Darryl, that's a *terrible* thing to say, and very, very unfair!" Melissa said hotly. "I happen to know that Bran . . . Mr. Kade spent a great deal of time deliberating whether to take this case or not." Melissa suddenly clamped her mouth shut, realizing she had said too much.

"And just how do you know that?" Darryl leaned toward her, an intensely curious expression in his eyes.

Melissa felt her color rising. "He's a friend of Julia Raymond, I mean Julia Lowell, my roommate while I was in law school. She mentioned it in a letter just this past week."

"Judge Raymond's daughter?"

"Yes," Melissa replied, fervently wishing she hadn't said anything.

"It's an interesting case," Darryl went on. "Are there going to be any surprise witnesses for the defense the media doesn't know about?"

"How on earth would I know anything about that?" she asked impatiently.

"I thought your friend might have mentioned it," he remarked, eyeing her closely. "I'd like to be the D.A. opposing Kade on this one. It would be the chance of a lifetime."

"It would be the chance of a lifetime to go down in defeat . . . *with* national coverage!" Melissa said heatedly.

"Is it that you think Kade is infallible or that I'm incompetent?" Darryl asked humorously, with a puzzled smile. "I thought with your interest in criminal law that you'd enjoy discussing the case. I had no idea you held such strong feelings about it, or that you could possibly consider it an open-and-shut case."

"I'm sorry that I snapped at you," Melissa said guiltily. "Maybe I'm just jealous of anyone who's in criminal law. I think I'd rather talk about myself tonight, if you don't mind."

"A subject I never tire of." Darryl flashed his pleasant

smile, his features immediately assuming an interested look inviting confidence. "Tell me what's on your mind."

"I'm unhappy," Melissa admitted. "I knew the first month or so I spent in the office I was just an intern, but after I passed the bar I thought I would assume a responsible role with the firm."

"And?" he encouraged.

"The only papers that cross my desk are routine contracts. Other people get the in-depth cases that need research. I'm not even included on the team." A look of annoyance crossed her features.

"Have you talked with Ross about your concerns?"

"Yes. He just said that my responsibilities would increase as I became better informed about the business. Tell me, how am I going to become informed if I'm not clued in to the situation? I have the distinct feeling that I'm nothing more than a figurehead." Melissa sighed heavily.

"I know how you feel," Darryl said. "I appreciate the training I got there in contracts and civil law, but I'm glad I left when I did. I'm afraid I would have settled into a complacent routine of shuffling papers and having two-martini lunches.

"Why don't you come work for me?" he suggested, a spark lighting his face. "We can't match your salary, but we sure can use you."

Melissa looked at him in surprise. She'd never considered that as a possibility. How would Laurence react after all the trouble he'd taken to fit her into the corporation? Darryl's offer stimulated her imagination.

"Do you really mean that? Are you sure it's not a case of creating another job for me?"

He shook his head. "I don't think the taxpayers are that indulgent," he said with a grin. "This is a serious proposition. We're snowed under and my staff works overtime just to handle the daily case load. You'd like them. For the most part they're a sharp young bunch."

She thought of his busy office, contrasting it to the hushed, still, uneventful surroundings of hers. "The only action in my office is the downhill skier on the wall—and even he's frozen in midflight." They laughed together.

"Seriously, will you consider it? I could keep you occupied if it's research you're interested in, but I'd want you in the courtroom as soon as possible. I don't think any male judge looking at you could resist your arguments for the prosecution."

"And do *you* always try to get female judges?" she asked sweetly.

"Touché," Darryl said with a disarming grin. "I really need you, Melissa. You're a good lawyer. And besides, you can raise my consciousness on valid feminist issues."

"Darryl, you're really quite a guy," Melissa said sincerely, wondering what peculiar perverseness would not allow her to love him. "But about your offer," she added after pondering seriously, "I can't do anything immediately. I'd have to lay a little groundwork first." Another undercover job for Irene, she thought. She'd have to solicit the housekeeper's subtle persuasive powers to help Laurence come around to the idea of her changing jobs.

"Well, think about it. You wouldn't be the boss's daughter," Darryl warned. "You'd have to put in some long days," he added thoughtfully, "and it would be difficult when you worked late evenings to get home through the snow, up those hills to your house. It would mean a lot of changes in your life-style."

"I'll think about changing jobs," Melissa replied. "But somehow I seriously doubt that I'll take you up on your offer, although I appreciate it."

"Do you have something else in mind?"

"I guess I do, although I haven't even admitted it to myself. You see, I'm really not interested in prosecution, and it would be a big step to leave the firm. If I do decide to make the break, I'm going all the way. What I've always wanted to be is a defense attorney. I want to help people who don't know the law and are afraid of appearing in court. I want to see to it that they get the rights and considerations that are theirs under the law."

"A defense attorney like Brandon Kade?"

"Hardly," she denied, averting her gaze. "I have no delusions of grandeur. I think the public defender's office would be a good place for me."

"Don't underrate your talents or ability, Melissa. That might be a good place to start, but you'll soon outgrow it. One of the good law firms will come knocking, and before long," he predicted, "we'll be playing on opposite sides of the net in earnest."

"I don't like to think of us as ever being opponents," Melissa protested. "Maybe I'm naïve, but I think the defense and the prosecution are a team, at least in a sense. One side representing the victim and the other the accused—but both working for true justice under the law."

"Unfortunately, Melissa, sometimes justice is a matter that money can buy. Take Kade, for an example. As I said before, anyone wealthy enough to retain him is virtually assured of being found not guilty."

"That's because he doesn't take a case unless his research assures him of his client's innocence. I don't believe he uses his legal skill to manipulate the system," she countered.

"Have you met the illustrious Mr. Kade?" Darryl asked, with open curiosity. "You seem to have very strong opinions where he's concerned."

"Yes, we've met," Melissa acknowledged uncomfortably, uneasy at having to mislead him, yet totally unwilling to discuss any part of her relationship with Brandon Kade. Each time Darryl interjected his name into the conversation it felt as though a knife was being stabbed into an unhealed wound.

"He was best man at Julia's wedding and he's a good friend of her father's. The judge has a high opinion of him,"

Melissa said. Then, deliberately changing the subject, she added, "Darryl, please don't mention what we've talked about to anyone. If I do decide to take another job I want to be the first to tell Dad."

"Of course I won't, sweetheart. I'm pleased you confided in me though. Come on, let's dance. This conversation has been a little heavy," he commented, leading her to the dance floor.

"You do understand how I feel about not wanting to work for you, don't you?" She spoke softly as they danced, his cheek against hers.

"Of course I do, Melissa, but I'm not going to give up trying to get you to play in my court, one way or the other. We make a great tennis double and I'm sure we'll make a great team on anything else we decide to do together." His meaning was unmistakable.

Even though she was held close in Darryl's arms, her body moving with his in perfect time to the music, Melissa knew something almost tangible had come between them. It wasn't that she preferred to be a defense attorney opposing the prosecution Darryl represented—it was the mention of Brandon Kade, the name and all that he still was to her, that was an iron wedge, slowly, inexorably forcing them apart.

CHAPTER ELEVEN

One day in late November Melissa sat at her desk staring at the sheaf of papers she held. I'm not going to take this, she fumed, indignantly slapping them down upon the polished surface. Rising abruptly, she stalked from the room. Tapping on Ross's private door, she turned the knob.

Ross rose from his desk, "What is it, Melissa?" he asked, a look of surprise crossing his face.

"I'm damn angry, Ross, and I'm sure you would be, too, if you were in my shoes." She kept her tone civil in spite of her pique.

"Sit down. Tell me what's bothering you."

"I prefer to stand. This isn't a social call. I've worked a whole week researching and clarifying that government directive for the issuance of our new stock . . ."

"You did a fine job," he interrupted. "Very thorough and concise."

"But you didn't trust me enough to accept my work," she accused.

The smile left his face. "What do you mean?"

"I just found out you gave the same assignment to Bill Adams."

"How do you know that?"

She certainly wasn't going to tell him that Adams's secretary had told hers. "That's not the point. Look, Ross, I don't need busy work, and if I'm not capable of pulling my weight around here I want to know it now."

"That has nothing to do with it. It's just that we run a tight ship. Taking one more hand aboard means we'll have to reshuffle the roster. Give us some time, Melissa—we'll work you in," he promised, putting all his charm into a fatherly smile.

She shook her head doubtfully. "I . . ."

"Excuse me, Mrs. Bennett"—the secretary's voice came over the intercom—"you have a call. Would you like to take it in there?"

"No, thank you, I'll take it in my own office. . . . Ross, I'd like to continue this discussion later."

"Certainly." He leaned over to check his calendar. "I'm tied up today, but are you free for lunch tomorrow?"

"Let me get back to you," she said, her hand on the doorknob.

Most likely it was Darryl calling, she thought, hurrying down the hall. He was another matter she was going to have to take care of soon. She'd given herself plenty of time where he was concerned, and it wasn't fair to keep him dangling any longer. The feelings just wouldn't come.

Dejectedly she picked up the phone.

"Melissa," Julia's excited voice rang out. "I hope I'm not interrupting anything important, but I had to call to tell you I'm pregnant! I just got the news."

"Julia, that's wonderful! I'm so happy for you and Scott." Melissa smiled. At least Julia's plans were working out for her, right on schedule, she thought without rancor.

"Melissa, do you think you and Jana could come down for a visit? Soon? I miss you so much. Scott's working around the clock with Brandon on the Dr. Pearson case, and frankly I'm lonely."

At the mention of Brandon's name Melissa's heart lurched painfully. She wanted to ask about him—wanted to savor the feel of his name on her tongue, but she couldn't trust her voice to remain casual.

"I miss you, too, Julia," she responded. "Believe me,

there's nothing going on here that I can't put on the back burner," she added cynically. "We'll be happy to come."

Why not? Her decision was impetuous, but if she were going to leave the firm, and that certainly seemed like the most viable option at the moment, going to San Francisco would help make the break easier.

They chatted a little longer; after Melissa hung up, a longing to see Brandon just once more flooded over her. And only with Julia could she pour out her painfully confused feelings. She needed desperately to talk with someone—she'd kept it all bottled up far too long. She dialed the number for airline reservations.

Julia and Scott's two-storied attached house fronted a steep-hilled street, opening in back onto an enclosed green yard full of late-blooming roses and sunshine.

Julia, thoughtful as always, had many welcoming gifts of toys and books for Jana.

"I hope I have a little girl," Julia remarked fondly, patting her flat abdomen as she watched Jana sitting on the living-room floor busily opening her packages.

"Fifty-fifty chance," Melissa laughed. "Either way, you can always try again."

After Julia had shown Melissa and Jana around the airy house decorated in sunburst yellow and shades of green, pointing out her wedding gifts, the two women went back to the living room, leaving Jana settled in front of *Sesame Street* in the den.

"Another wedding present," Julia remarked, pouring white wine from an ornate crystal decanter after they'd seated themselves on the couch. "How are things going for you, Melissa? You look terrific . . . but you're so thin. And you seem preoccupied. What's wrong?" she asked quietly.

In a rush of words it all came out—her concerns about Darryl and his growing attachment to her, her frustrations about her career, and the difficulties involved if she chose to leave the firm.

Julia listened, candidly putting in an encouraging word or two, but still Melissa held back from talking about the man uppermost in her mind. Seeing Julia had brought it all back as if it had happened yesterday—as if the past months of torture had been nothing more than a sleepless night's bad dream, reawakening memories too sweetly bitter to absorb.

"You do have a lot to think about," Julia summed up pensively. "Sometimes talking about what's bothering me helps me reach a decision. Maybe it will you too. . . . I haven't even asked about Laurence. How is he?"

"He's fine, and so's Irene. They make a wonderful couple. I hope he has sense enough to realize what he has there." It was a relief to talk about someone else.

"Do you mean romantically?" Julia asked, surprise widening her smoky eyes.

"Yes, I do," Melissa stated emphatically. "She's a cultured, attractive woman and absolutely devoted to him. He couldn't do better."

"That's great. And you, Melissa—is . . . is Brandon the reason that Darryl doesn't have a chance?"

The stricken look on Melissa's face as she rose to stand silhouetted against the windowed courtyard door told it all. Julia moved to stand beside her.

"I'm sorry I was so blunt. Do you want to talk about it?" She put her arm around Melissa's shoulder, drawing her back toward the sofa. "Confession is good for the soul," she quoted earnestly. "You've never kept anything from me before, but you've been reluctant to talk about Brandon ever since you met him. You're in love with him, aren't you?"

"Yes," Melissa admitted, glad of a chance to share the heavy load of grief that lay on her soul with someone who cared. "I'm in love with him, and figuratively speaking, it's killing me."

"Killing you? What do you mean?" Julia asked in alarm, knowing Melissa was not given to exaggeration.

"He proposed to me on the boat . . . and I told him no," Melissa said quietly, flatly, choking back emotion. "It was too soon. We had too many things to work out, and he wouldn't wait. Now I wish to God I hadn't made the decision I did. Oh, Julia, I'm so confused. I want him so much. I'm willing to take him any way I can have him. Life seems impossible without him."

"And how were things left?" Julia asked.

"They're finished," Melissa answered bleakly. "We haven't spoken since that last night."

"That explains a lot of things," Julia commented, almost to herself. "When I called him to tell him that you and Jana were coming, I thought he'd be delighted, but—" her voice trailed off.

"But, what?" Melissa demanded.

"Well"—Julia struggled to go on—"he said he was very busy, but he'd try to find time to see Jana. I assumed he meant both of you, except . . . he did seem to stress Jana, now that I think of it."

"I hope he will see her," Melissa said quickly. "She loves him and misses him a great deal. He paid so much attention to her in La Jolla I almost think he's become a father figure for her."

"But"—Julia hesitated—"tell me, why did you turn him down? You can't deny that you love him."

Melissa leaned from the sofa to put her goblet on the tray. Sitting on the edge of the couch, she clasped her arms across her chest as though suddenly cold in the warm room.

"I fell in love with him the night we met," she began, her eyes directed to the floor. "In La Jolla I knew I loved him totally and that my life would never be the same again."

She leaned back against the couch, releasing her arms from the tight clasp of her hands. Her face clouded, and a frown appeared on her smooth brow. "That evening driving back from the airport after your wedding, we argued about his attitude toward women." She didn't want to tell Julia what he'd said about the threat he thought Julia's proposed career presented to the success of her marriage. "He left without seeing me the next morning."

Agitated, she stood up as the most agonizing scenes of all passed through her memory. Walking again toward the French doors, she turned to face Julia, her arms clasped across her breasts once more. "He joined us in Seattle, but his attitude hadn't changed at all. When he proposed, I turned him down. It was as though he expected I would join his life, but he wouldn't join mine. It was almost as if he wanted me as a possession . . . not as a person. I couldn't marry him like that . . . even though I love him as I have never loved anyone." Her voice wavered.

Julia nodded in understanding. "Melissa, you were right to refuse him. In fact, you had no other choice." She thought for a few moments, and then said, "You both need more time. You need to talk this out with each other. I'm sure you could reach an understanding. I know Brandon is difficult and usually wants things his own way, but he's not completely unreasonable and unwilling to compromise."

"Mommy, come here," Jana called, her voice shrill with excitement. "Uncle Brandon and Uncle Scott are on TV. Hurry!"

Melissa and Julia arrived in time to see a parting shot of Brandon and Scott entering a car with Dr. Pearson between them. Even the slight glimpse she'd caught of his familiar figure sent shock waves through Melissa's overwrought system. Her hand sought the heavy medallion at her breast as she tried to concentrate on the commentator's words.

"Is Uncle Brandon here?" Jana interrupted, a hopeful smile lighting her face.

"Yes," Julia answered somewhat reluctantly. "In fact he'll be here for a quick dinner tonight." She glanced anxiously at Melissa. "I really should have told you before this, but I couldn't find a good opening." She grimaced. "He and Scott stop by for a quick bite each evening before going back to . . ." Her voice trailed off uncertainly.

The broadcaster's voice flowed glibly as he went on to his next story. Melissa's attention was caught by the mention of Anchorage. Forcing herself to concentrate on the photograph of a young woman whose body had been found on the ski slopes of one of Anchorage's most popular resorts, Melissa could only register a few details—"gruesome murder . . . suspect still at large"—before the anchorman went on to other news. She had a fleeting thought of Darryl and what this would mean to his already understaffed office, before she felt Jana's arms around her waist.

"Goody, goody. Uncle Brandon's coming to see us!"

Melissa held her daughter closely as her troubled eyes sought Julia's. How ironic that Julia's announcement could at once bring such happiness to Jana and such tumultuous reluctance to her.

Melissa's first impulse was to stay in her room during dinner, but she knew that would be utterly inappropriate—embarrassing to all the others. She had to take the bull by the horns. She smiled at the appropriate metaphor, thinking of the stubbornness of the man she dreaded to see. Yet why was she here? Why had she come if not because she hoped that somehow she would see him again? If I stay up here, she reasoned, I might just as well be in Anchorage.

And yet, what did she hope could come of their meeting? That they would be reconciled? Yes, she hoped that with all her heart. But was she ready to open Pandora's box and let the precious gift of hope escape? If reconciliation was impossible, did she need to see her hope die—to realize, once and for all, that there was nothing left between them? Yes, that was it, she decided. She had to know one way or the other. If he loved her, she wanted him . . . was ready to give her life to him. If not? . . . She wanted release. If finally I see that

I mean nothing to him, maybe I can begin to rebuild my life, she told herself.

Squaring her slight shoulders, she went down the stairs.

When Scott's key clicked in the door, Jana was there. In one swoop she was in Brandon's arms, nearly strangling him with hugs.

"I saw you on TV," she squealed by way of greeting, as he carried her into the rattan-and-antique-furnished living room.

Heart pounding, Melissa watched him approach, her hands growing cold and clammy in panic. His vibrancy engulfed her, evoking bittersweet memories. Emotion choked her throat. His slate-blue eyes met hers over Jana's head with an impenetrable inscrutability. Acknowledging her presence with a distant nod and a cool glance, he directed his remarks to Julia, leaving Melissa feeling as if she'd been hit with a frigid blast of arctic air.

For Melissa the quick dinner was a frosty affair. A cold knot formed in her stomach. Julia and Scott tried to conduct a pleasant conversation, but a silent glacial tension increased between Melissa and Brandon with frightening intensity. Melissa felt as though she'd been frozen and would shatter into a million brittle pieces if she so much as moved. Fortunately, Jana didn't notice, because most of what conversation there was revolved around her. I hardly expected him to welcome me with open arms, she thought with growing despair, but I didn't realize he would be so openly hostile. She was shocked that he didn't even bother to cover his feelings with a thin veneer of politeness.

After the men had left and Jana had been put to bed, Julia took Melissa into her own bedroom. "Now, sit down on the bed like we used to do," she directed.

Then without preamble she began. "It's obvious Brandon's as miserable as you are. He wouldn't have treated you the way he did if he weren't hurting badly. I've never seen him behave like that. I'm glad you told me what happened between you before he got here. I know Scott's puzzled, but I promised I'd explain things to him tonight.

"But Melissa, Brandon couldn't get enough of looking at you. I caught him watching you while you helped Jana fill her plate. He barely touched his dinner. Go after him, Melissa, if you're sure that's what you want. I know what the problem is: his pride is hurt, and he'll never take the first step. I love you both, dearly." Her voice softened. "I can't stand by watching the two of you suffer like this."

"I don't know what I want," Melissa managed to say through numb, stiff lips. She should take heart at the encouragement in Julia's words, but facing the implaccable man with his chilling reserve had convinced her of his final rejection.

As the days passed and the trial wound down to its final phases, Melissa and Julia filled their time Christmas shopping in the elegantly decorated department stores and boutiques. There were no more quick "at home" dinners, with Brandon stopping by with Scott after work. Frequently Melissa and Julia met Scott at an exclusive out-of-the-way restaurant before taking in a musical, ballet, or symphony.

Obsessed with thoughts of Brandon, Melissa's mind gave her no peace. I love him more than ever, she realized, if that's possible. I belong to him, as he said, as surely as if he'd placed a ring upon my finger.

Each time she and Julia went out, she longed to catch sight of him walking by chance on the busy downtown streets. Knowledge of his very nearness stirred the aching passions he'd aroused in her body with his tenderness and demanding ardor. Her nights virtually sleepless, tormented at best, she yearned with every fiber of her being to erase the expressionless stare in the once loving eyes that confronted her each time her memory recalled his face.

Julia, Melissa, and Jana crowded in front of the TV to witness the acquittal of Dr. Todd Pearson. Brandon had scored another stunning victory. Melissa watched as Brandon made a few perfunctory remarks to the press in his deep, melodious voice before escorting his client from the courthouse. Her heart ached with longing as she watched him on the screen, so much in control and so incredibly handsome.

"Now that that's finally over," Julia announced, "maybe I'll have my husband back for the holidays. It's time to start on a new case though: *Bennett v. Kade.* I've been thinking of little else, and I think I've developed a plausible strategy. Come sit down with me, Melissa. I'm really worried about you. It gets worse all the time, doesn't it?"

Melissa nodded mutely in reply, the lump in her throat almost too large to allow words to escape. "Seeing you and Scott married and settled in this fantastic city has almost made it unbearable to think of what I gave up. I could have been Brandon's wife by now—we might even have been your neighbors." Her voice caught in a half sob. "Everything else in my life seemed so important when I refused to marry him. Now nothing else matters."

"That's what I thought. Has it ever occurred to you that he doesn't know you've changed your mind? Everything might be different if he did. You should be telling all this to him, instead of to me."

"I don't know," Melissa replied despondently, fingering the slender gold chains at her neck. "I think he's made it clear he doesn't want to see me."

Julia stood in a show of assertiveness, determination in her voice. "He doesn't know how you feel. After Scott gets home tonight, I'm going to drive you over to Brandon's condominium, and"—she was emphatic—"you're going to talk with him!"

"His condo! I—I can't do that!" Melissa stammered.

"Yes, you can," Julia countered firmly. "That way you'll be in control of the situation. I just read in some magazine or another that if you want to have it out with someone the best thing to do is to go to their place. That way they can't walk out on you."

Despite her unhappiness, Melissa couldn't stop a short laugh, though she shook her head negatively. "Leave it to you to come up with logic like that!"

Agitated, Melissa continued to shake her head as they discussed it further, but Julia calmly persisted, overruling her objections.

Desperate, thinking that nothing Brandon could say or do would make her feel any worse than she already felt, Melissa finally agreed.

Dressing carefully in a simple gray cashmere knit that clung to her shapely form, Melissa slipped on her silver mink jacket. The Aztec Sun Stone, glinting like a ray of hope in the muted light of her room, nestled against the soft curve of her breasts. Remembering the look of love she'd seen in Brandon's eyes when he'd given it to her, she fervently hoped that tonight she would see it there again.

Outside the impressive high-rise condominium, Julia pushed the button under Brandon Kade's number. An answering buzz immediately opened the automatic lock.

"He must be expecting someone," Julia remarked as they pushed open the heavy glass doors.

"Then maybe this isn't a good time," Melissa said anxiously. "Let's go home."

"No. We've come this far. It's no time for cold feet," Julia insisted, propelling her reluctant friend toward the elevator. "He's on the top floor. I'll wait for you down here," she said firmly, indicating the spacious well-furnished foyer. "If you're not down in twenty minutes, I'll go on home."

"If I'm not down in twenty minutes, you'd better call the police," Melissa retorted between clenched teeth as she stepped into the waiting elevator. "I feel like an Aztec virgin being led up to a stone altar, in imminent danger of having my heart cut from my breast." She touched the gold necklace at her chest.

"You're a very beautiful sacrifice," Julia answered, "but not quite qualified." With a wry grin, Melissa nervously joined her giggle.

The heavy oak door silently slid closed, shutting out Julia's smiling encouragement. Melissa was seized with apprehension as the elevator smoothly ascended to the top floor. Perhaps he wasn't home. Perhaps she wouldn't have to confront him with evidence of the tumultuous pleadings of her wayward heart. Then she realized how absurd that notion was: he must be home because he'd responded to the buzzer.

Stepping from the elevator, she stood facing the blank door of his penthouse. Why am I doing this? she wondered. Weak with anticipation, she placed a hand over her midriff, hoping to calm the butterflies fluttering there. The knowledge that Brandon was on the other side of the wall was enough to sustain her in her desperate purpose, was enough to crowd her mind with bright visions of the rapturous moments spent with him.

Her mouth thirsted for the honeyed moisture of the sensuous lips that alone could quench her raw burning desire; her eyes sought the perfection of the manly face and form that provoked an esthetic response like no other; her ears longed to hear the deep, melodious drawl. There was no way she could turn from the hope that this would all be hers . . . no way she could turn back to the lonely bleakness of existence without him.

But what can I say to him? she thought outrageously, her throat constricted and dry. What can I say to that proud vital man to make him understand that I can't go on without him? That I love him without limits and that I want him without reservation? A cold fear tingled down her spine. In all their discussions she and Julia had never dealt with the question of what she would say or do when she actually confronted the stubbornly enigmatic man she loved. This is like going into court to defend a client without having prepared an opening argument or defense, she realized. *I can't go through with this!*

As she turned to flee in panic, the door of the penthouse opened without warning to reveal Brandon in a white dress shirt unbuttoned at the throat, a silk tie hanging loosely around his tanned neck. Melissa stood, surprised and stunned at his sudden appearance, until she realized he must have heard the elevator stop at his floor and been puzzled that no one had rung. From the startled look on his face, it was clear Melissa Collins Bennett was the last person in the world he'd expected to find in the corridor. Behind her she barely heard the electronic door slide shut as the elevator automatically descended, cutting off her only avenue of escape.

Unceremoniously, Brandon motioned for her to enter. "What the devil are you doing here?" he asked harshly, although his eyes held hers intently. "I was expecting my secretary."

The angles of his familiar face appeared hard in the shadowy raised entry, where she and Brandon stood a heartbeat apart, three plushly carpeted steps up from the huge living room. Tearing her eyes from the riveting steel-blue of his, prolonging the moment of truth, Melissa took in the room at a glance. Lights of the city and of the gorgeous Golden Gate Bridge sparkled through a wall of window at the far side of the dimly lit room. Starkly modern, expensive chrome, leather, and glass furnishings were set on white carpet below a cathedral ceiling that rose dramatically, two stories high. She noticed boldly vivid contemporary paintings filling one wall, vaguely aware of the strains of Beethoven's Seventh Symphony playing softly in the background.

"I . . . I had to see you," Melissa stammered plaintively, her lower lip trembling.

"What for?" Brandon retorted, grasping her soft upper arms.

The command in his tone tore the answer from her throat. "Because I love you," she whispered, expressing the thought her mind had held since she had first laid eyes on him. "Because I'm miserable without you. Because—" She faltered, knowing her words were wasted against his flint-hard resistance.

No encouraging softening of the lines of his face met her whispered confession. It was as if he hadn't even heard her. Suddenly conscious of the pent-up power emanating from him, she finished lamely, "Jana needs you."

His face flushed with anger as his hands released her. "Jana?" he questioned disbelievingly. "She has me any time she needs me, and she knows that. You could take a lesson from that little lady. She accepts people as they are, which is more than I can say for her mother." His voice was heavy with hurt outrage.

"Brandon, I can understand why you're angry . . . why you'd never want to see me again. I know the pain I've caused you." That we've caused each other, she finished silently. Why had she feared her heart would be cut from her body by a savage priest at the top of a stony pyramid? Her fears had been foolish . . . after the fact. Her heart was no longer hers . . . she'd given it to this man long ago. "I want us to be together. I'm willing to give in on any point that would make that possible," Melissa heard herself saying, unconsciously raising pleading arms to him.

"You don't need to surrender your precious woman's rights for me," he said coldly, backing away from her touch. "You had your choice and you chose your damned career. Well, sleep with that and see how warm it keeps you."

"I can't sleep—I can't do anything but think of you." Dying inside, she hated her weakness, but she couldn't suppress the words.

"It passes," he replied. He stepped back as though watching the effect of his words before callously suggesting, "Take out your law books and read them until you fall asleep."

He was hurting her, hurting her badly, but she could stand this retaliation for his own pain, if only when his controlled tirade were over he would take her in his strong arms . . . kiss the bitter words from her memory. Knowing his pride had suffered a blow when she'd refused to marry him on his terms, she'd been prepared for some resistance. Still, she'd counted on the passionate bond they'd shared so long ago under the stars to at least make him open to reason. But he hadn't moved except to avoid her touch and continued to stand implacably before her, maddeningly near.

Swallowing the last tattered remnant of self-restraint, she tried once more. Her voice was stifled, stilted. "Brandon, try to understand. I had to go home to Alaska. I owed it to my father-in-law."

"Now it's your father-in-law, next it'll be your Aunt Tilly or whoever. Don't you have a mind of your own?" he argued senselessly. "You're wasting your time and mine. I told you before, Melissa: I don't like arguing outside the courtroom. I meant it. Case closed."

Rooted to the floor, she stared at him in disbelief, clenching her hands until her nails bit into the softness of her palms. Case closed? Was that all she was to him now? Nothing more than another conquest duly stamped and filed away? An eternity passed, but her leaden legs refused to move.

The space between them was charged with a current of emotion, exerting an inexplicable power to both repel and attract. She watched as conflicting emotions played across his face: it was all there: pain, anger, humiliation—a flash of naked yearning and love? There was no time for thought. As if compelled by the magnetic force, Brandon moved, grasped her slight shoulders roughly, and pulled her stunned body tightly to his, trapping her arms between them. Crushingly his mouth came down on hers. Incongruously a faint whiff of after-shave pleasantly assailed her nostrils before the rough stubble of a long day's growth of whiskers ground into her tender face as he forced her lips apart, furiously probing the tender depths of her mouth. His kiss was punishing—a verdict allowing no appeal. The music in the background rose and swelled to a crashing crescendo as his hands continued to hold her in a viselike grip. As rashly as he had taken it, he released her resisting body, causing her to lose her balance and stumble backward.

"Or is that what you came up here for?" the powerful stranger asked, his steely voice mockingly scornful.

Involuntarily her hand shot out, striking the granite hardness of his face with all the strength she could muster. The act was a futile instinctive effort to change the hateful expression carved in its lines. The sharp slap sounded like a gunshot in the muted room. He didn't move. He didn't even raise his hand to the place where her handprint was beginning to redden across his cheek. Tears spilled from her eyes as she watched the mark darken to a deep ugly hue—felt the mark of his rejection blot out her hope . . . but not the anguish of her love.

The sound of the doorbell broke the bitter silence of confusion between them. Reaching past her, Brandon opened the door. Melissa turned to see a tall blonde standing in the hallway.

"Oh, I hope I'm not interrupting anything. I used my key, but I see I should have buzzed." The smiling woman's face sobered to concern.

"Not at all," Brandon replied briskly. "I've been expecting you."

"I was just leaving," Melissa choked out.

Without knowing how she got there, Melissa found herself in the hall as the door shut irrevocably behind her. A devastating wave of humiliation swept over her as she sank back against the door for support. Having tried and failed, she was defeated.

She touched her lips, still hurting from the bruising pressure of his mouth. Crossing her arms over her breasts she lightly stroked her upper arms still sore from the grip of his fingers. Looking down in a daze, she saw the hand that still stung from the reflexive blow she had delivered. Her ears ringing, echoing the crashing crescendo of emotion-filled music, she stumbled into the waiting elevator, blindly fumbling for the foyer button.

The secretary was quickly sent on her way. High above the city there was no one to witness Brandon Kade, ordinarily so tightly controlled, as he angrily grasped an antique vase and violently threw it against the white brick of his fireplace, shattering it into countless tinkling fragments.

He was furious—furious with Melissa and furious with himself! Blood pounded through his veins, making his head throb. How could one small woman cause him such continual anguish! She was infuriating beyond reason. Her sudden appearance at his door had been staggeringly unanticipated. Her physical presence in San Francisco had been upsetting enough without her actually coming to his place and forcing an issue that he'd thought was dead and buried.

He'd gotten over her, he told himself, taking a calming breath. It had been difficult but not impossible. He'd been used to deprivations from his childhood, and even though certain unfulfilled desires had burned within his breast, he'd learned to carry on. He'd learned early to bury his emotions and to conceal his hurt rather than to rail against fate.

Hell! Did Melissa think just because she'd changed her mind that he was at her beck and call? He had plans to spend the holidays with the Raymonds, as usual, and then to go to Acapulco for a few weeks. Melissa was not going to spoil that, he vowed. He paced rapidly back and forth, bright memories of La Jolla rising to mind. He'd considered that home for many years. The estate had been his to go to for relaxation and companionship. Now that bewitching little blonde had taken that from him; it would never be the same. Memories of Melissa and Jana at La Jolla were etched indelibly on his consciousness. He would see their lovely faces, hear their lilting voices at every turn. No matter how little he wanted to admit it to himself, it was true. Trite but true: she'd gotten under his skin.

Striding purposely to the mirrored bar, he poured himself a stiff drink, the muscle still working angrily in his jaw. Glowering out over the lights of the beautiful city, he tightly gripped a crystal tumbler. She was somewhere down there . . . an undeniably beautiful, passionate woman. But still just a woman. What did he care? Damn it, he did care, he groaned. Just the thought of her stirred the embers of his desire to flame. And he'd had her. He'd had her right here in his arms and his damnable pride had driven her away. All of his life he'd sought only the best and he'd had it all—had it on his own terms and in his own time. His professional success had exceeded even his wildest expectations. But now the one thing he'd wanted most in life, the thing he couldn't buy, couldn't win . . . was escaping him. Incredibly, escaping him because of some missing key, some understanding that he lacked.

Look at me—a two-time loser, he derided himself, taking a deep drink from the glass he held. The only comfort he could find in the whole mess was that at least this romantic failure hadn't been publicized in the papers for everyone in the world to gloat over.

After replenishing his drink, he prowled restlessly before the large windows. She wasn't good for him anyway. Everything about her had been too confusing from the beginning. He still found himself distracted from his work by thoughts of her. Like a moonstruck lover, he'd spent hours wondering what she was doing in Alaska . . . and whom she was doing it with. For him there'd been no other women since he'd met her. Somehow the appeal just wasn't there. He knew, as much as he hated to admit it, that he'd been measuring each one against the image of Melissa Collins Bennett's petite frame, laughing eyes, keen intelligence, and loving disposition. None of them had measured up.

Ever since Julia had informed him of Melissa's visit his mind had been a shambles. It was a good thing that Dr. Pearson's case had been in its final stages and really out of his hands, or there was no telling what verdict might have come down, he thought wryly, as the warm effects of the amber cognac began to calm him.

Lord knows he'd wanted to see that Alaskan Snowbird, but with the typical confusion she caused him, he hadn't wanted to see her. At Julia's apartment whenever he'd picked up Jana, he'd had to steel himself against the attraction Melissa held for him. Each time he'd seen her it had become more and more difficult, more feverishly painful

His anger was dissipated as his thoughts began to mellow. The scenario of the evening passed before his eyes. Melissa's appearance at his door had caught him completely off guard. He could handle an impersonal courtroom battle with ease, and no true ill will. But nothing had ever touched him—come so near to his core—as his conflict with Melissa. He'd never before let anyone in so close to his feelings, feelings he'd been sure he'd left behind in his childhood. He'd never found himself so irrational, so vulnerable. The very shock of the encounter had left him so unprepared that the substance of their dialogue escaped him. Like an angry child, he'd lashed out, taking out his frustrations on the object of his confusion, incapable of listening to reason, concerned only with himself and his own reactions.

He sank into the leather couch, running his hand through the back of his hair. Had she said she loved him? He thought she had. He tried to think . . . to remember what exactly she had said. Were they really the words he'd waited for her to say? Had wanted her to say that night on the boat when he'd thought Melissa would be his? Would be his—the words echoed in his mind. Could he say that Warren was Grace's, that Grace was Warren's? Absurd! He'd never considered ownership when he thought of the two of them. Grace was Warren's wife, but that dignified lady was her own person . . . certainly not her husband's possession. Was there a moral to this parallel? What did he expect from Melissa? That she would belong to him? He'd turned deaf ears tonight when she'd offered just that, he realized with sharp self-recrimination. He raised his hand to his still-stinging cheek. He'd deserved that slap . . . and damn it, he admired the woman with spunk enough to do it. *That* was the woman he loved. If that was the case, he sure as hell had a lot of rethinking to do.

Should he call her? He reached for the phone, but let his arm drop. What would he say? He wasn't ready. He needed time. Lord, how he hoped there was time, time to think how to win her back. Memories of the brutish way he'd forced himself on her in his fury, insulting her with his degrading kiss, nearly convinced him that his actions had canceled any feeling she would ever have for him. He'd been given another chance and he'd blown it . . . blown it like a damn fool! He heard his voice shouting: Case closed. . . . If only it were! He groaned again. . . . Lord, how he loved that woman. The next move would be up to him, and it would have to be good.

CHAPTER TWELVE

Looking down through the early darkness of the arctic winter as their plane descended toward the Anchorage airport, Melissa pointed out to her little daughter that the ribbons of multicolored lights delineating the runways looked like a gigantic, geometric Christmas tree spread out to welcome them home. Their plane touched down, sped past huge banks of the snow that had fallen steadily while they were in California, and came to a stop on the carefully plowed and salted concourse in front of the terminal. Melissa felt a peculiar heaviness come over her—rising from her seat was as difficult as emerging from the buoyancy of a pool of water into the weighty press of gravity.

Their unpremeditated departure from San Francisco had been so hasty—and so upsetting—that Melissa hadn't called home to announce her change in plans. So there were no smiling relatives to greet them among the throngs of holiday travelers being warmly welcomed into the arms of their families and loved ones. Somehow that circumstance, which she could have easily avoided with a quick phone call, added to the bleak feeling of being unwanted that filled her heart. She ached with a lonely misery that permeated her bones.

As Melissa and Jana took a taxi through the festively decorated city and on up into the snow-covered foothills toward home, she bravely assumed a false gaiety, preparing to face Irene and Laurence. The look of worried concern on Julia's face, when they had parted in San Francisco a few hours earlier, had determined her not to make others uncomfortable in her presence. But would the infectious goodwill of the approaching Christmas season help her through the despairing ordeal of recovering from a doomed love affair, she wondered? Or would the holidays drive her still further into the state of depression that threatened to overtake her? Glancing at the clean profile of her daughter's little face, Melissa felt her heart sink with guilt. Jana's life hadn't stopped—it was all ahead of her. If for no other reason, Melissa thought, I have to find the courage to get through this for her sake. She deserves that independent strong mother I've promised myself I'll be. Damn it, Melissa resolved, I'll make it!

Driving onto the grounds of the Bennett home, the spectacle of the long low house completely outlined with blue lights greeted them as Melissa and Jana peered through the steamy windows of the taxi. Tall spruce trees glowed with twinkling white lights that lay hidden among their snow-laden branches. Candles shone warmly, beckoningly, from green-wreathed bay windows.

Although surprised by their unannounced return, Laurence and Irene warmly and enthusiastically welcomed the travel-worn pair into the pine-scented home. In spite of her resolve, tears threatened dangerously near the surface as Melissa felt the comfort of Irene's arms when the older woman gave her a particularly personal greeting—Melissa suspected Irene could read the underlying sadness that lurked in her eyes. Melissa clung tightly to Laurence and buried her face against his staunch chest when he enveloped her in a hearty bear hug.

Brandy, exuberant at her tiny mistress's return, joyously followed at Jana's heels, tail wagging, soft brown eyes full of love. Watching Jana, Melissa realized her daughter was fully satisfied with her unconventional family. Jana looked upon Brandon only as a happy addition to the circle of those she loved and demanded nothing more from him than he was willing to give. Why, oh, why, Melissa asked herself plaintively, couldn't I have been satisfied with the same when he offered to share his life with me on that summer's night?

In her bedroom unpacking the gaily wrapped packages she'd carried with her from the shops and boutiques of the cosmopolitan city, Melissa found herself gazing unseeingly out the small paned windows of her room. This has to stop, she chided herself. She'd looked forward to this special Christmas more than any in memory—she was not going to find it tarnished and lacking in luster. My infatuation with Brandon Kade has controlled my life since the moment we met, she admitted silently, but it is not going to spoil my family's holidays too.

Words, words, she sighed, sinking to her chaise longue; easily spoken, yet powerless to alter feelings. But this is the way things are, she told herself sternly, rising from the chair to dress for dinner. I've no choice but to rid my mind of thoughts of him. I owe it to Jana to make this the best Christmas she's ever had. This is the first Christmas since she was a baby that I won't have to dash in and out of her life like Santa's reindeer, Melissa thought with a faint smile.

Sensing an undertone of excitement charging the atmosphere at the table that evening, Melissa at first supposed it to be generated by their homecoming, but the odd sense of expectancy seemed to build throughout the meal. She noticed that Irène, attractively dressed in a long red hostess gown, smiled broadly but ate little of the deliciously prepared dinner. Laurence's behavior was off a little too—she couldn't put her finger on just what it was, but something was clearly in the wind.

After dinner, assuming almost a conspiratorial air, Laurence led the three of them into the living room, where a magnificent noble fir, bedecked with handcrafted ornaments and tied with a myriad of red velvet bows, shed a warm glow of light. Jana cried out in awe and clapped her hands at the sight.

Waiting on the low oak coffee table, beside a spreading red-blossomed poinsettia plant, were a bottle of fine champagne and three crystal champagne glasses sparkling in the firelight. Brandy lay stretched out on the hearthrug in complete contentment as though all the splendor were for her alone. Melissa gave a puzzled shrug of her shoulders in response to Jana's gaze, which clearly questioned what this unusual ceremony might mean, although a hopeful suspicion began to grow in her heart.

After the cork had popped and the adults' glasses were filled, Laurence stood with his ramrod back to the fire, raised his glass in toast, and proclaimed huskily, "To Irene, the woman I love." He drank deeply.

Irene's fair Nordic skin blushed rosily at Melissa and Jana's shocked stares of surprise. So, Melissa thought as she raised her glass, it was to be as she had hoped. The two were ideally suited for one another.

Beaming down upon the women seated before him, Laurence unnecessarily cleared his throat. "Irene and I are going to be married."

"How wonderful!" Melissa exclaimed with pleasure as she jumped up to hug first Irene and then Laurence, thinking how very appropriate her gift of the exquisite negligee she had purchased for Irene in San Francisco would be now. "When's the wedding?" she asked in excitement, putting her arm affectionately around Irene.

"As soon as possible," Laurence replied expansively, giving his intended bride a fond look. Pure happiness lit Irene's face as her eyes held his in a look of loving tenderness.

"But this will always be your home," Laurence added hastily to Melissa and Jana. "That will never change."

"Now you'll really be my nana forever and ever." Jana squeezed Irene tightly around the neck.

"That's right, darling." Irene's voice choked with emotion. Her eyes filled with tears of happiness and relief as she hugged the child closely. Melissa was sure any unfounded doubts Irene must have had about their willingness to accept her into the family had evaporated like the bubbles from the sparkling champagne.

I was right to wait, Melissa thought. Having planned to announce her decision to join the public defenders' staff—made during the flight back from San Francisco—something had prevented her from bringing the subject up during dinner. She was glad now that she hadn't let it intrude upon the evening, even though she knew Laurence's announcement might complicate her own plans. There was considerable danger that he and Irene might think her decision to leave the firm and move out on her own had been caused by their decision to marry. Nothing could be further from the truth. In fact, Laurence's marriage would actually assuage the guilt she'd felt at the thought of leaving him alone.

But all that would have to be dealt with later. The moment belonged solely to Irene and Laurence and their plans for the future. Everyone agreed they would be married in a small intimate ceremony at the house on New Year's Day with a large reception at Laurence's club. Melissa was delighted to learn that the honeymooners planned to travel for a few weeks in Europe, as she knew that many of the years of Laurence's life had been lonely without a loving companion. All that would change with Irene at his side.

With more than a little dread, Melissa gradually realized she would have to confront her father-in-law with her own plans immediately. I can't take the chance of his hearing them from anyone else and having his happiness marred by feelings that I've betrayed him, she thought.

Jana lay sleeping next to Brandy on the rug in front of the fire as they finished the last of the champagne. Irene tenderly helped the groggy child to her feet and led her from the room, brushing off Melissa's attempt to help.

"I haven't had the chance to put her to bed for a long time, and I've missed her. I know you're tired from your trip. You stay here and keep Laurence company for a while."

Obediently, Melissa sank back on the couch, crossing her legs. Her knees felt weak, her limbs heavy. Rather than lifting her spirits, the wine, coupled with persistent, nagging thoughts of Brandon that wouldn't leave her mind, had drugged her into lassitude. Glancing obliquely at the openly concerned face of her father-in-law, she was overwhelmed with a guilt as intense as that she'd experienced earlier when looking at Jana.

He'd been so honest, so trusting and confident that she and Jana would lovingly accept his plans for his own happiness. She was glad their response could be so freely and satisfactorily given—at least she'd done that much. Uncrossing her legs, she shifted uneasily on the couch. I haven't been giving Laurence as much credit as he's given me, she realized unhappily. I've just assumed he'd be resistant to my plans. I've got to tell him.

She hadn't felt as uncomfortable in this generous man's presence since the first time Sonny had brought her home to meet his dad, what seemed like a lifetime ago. Laurence and she had gone through a lot together. He'd been as supportive and loving to her as if she'd been his own daughter.

Why was she so afraid to speak the words that would test his willingness to let her be her own person? Because, she answered herself, I've never put him to the test. The constraints he's placed upon my life and Jana's have been so reasonable it would have been ridiculous to fight them. Actually, she admitted, as hard to accept as some things were at the time, virtually everything he's done has always been in my own best interests. The one thing I permitted him to dictate was that I was to practice corporate rather than criminal law when I returned. And it was I who meekly acquiesced to that restriction—there was no way he would have insisted over firm protests—she knew that now.

Laurence crossed the room in long, easy strides and seated

himself beside his daughter-in-law. "What's the matter, Melissa?" he questioned, his face troubled. "You seem upset. Is it because of Irene and me?"

"Oh, no, Dad. How could you think that? To be honest, I've been hoping this would happen. I'm truly happy for both of you." A wan smile touched her lips as tears spilled from her eyes. She quickly looked away from his probing gaze.

"I'm relieved to hear that. Actually I hadn't really worried about it until just a few minutes ago. I've been sure you knew nothing could change the way I feel about you. But if it's not that, then what is it? Irene has some idea there's a young man in San Francisco you're interested in. Is there anything I can do to help that situation along? Offer him a job? Help him relocate?" She mutely shook her head in reply.

"Has he hurt you?" His voice suddenly dangerous, his eyes narrowed to slits.

Melissa's heart turned with love as she reached out to take his hands in hers. "No, Dad. It's not that that's bothering me. I'm afraid I'm going to hurt you. You must know how much I love you and I never want to disappoint you. As I've said to myself, so many times, I owe everything to you."

"Listen, sugar, you don't owe me a thing. I'm the one who couldn't have gone on without you." His eyes clouded briefly with sad memories before clearing to their usual brightness. "That nursery down the hall holds the greatest gift you could have ever given me, tucked into that little bed we picked out together. No amount of money could ever buy that."

Melissa winced; her courage wavered. She wanted to stop the conversation . . . to turn from the love in his eyes. Nervously she rose to her feet; walking toward the fire, she held her hands out to its comforting warmth. Perhaps it would be easier to say what she must if she placed some physical distance between them. She heard him rise behind her.

"Darryl's offered me a job, but . . . I turned him down." The words were blunt, flatly spoken.

"So? What's the punchline? I can feel there's one coming."

Her shoulders hunched involuntarily as she continued to stare into the fire for a long moment. Taking a deep breath, she turned, straightening her small frame to its full height. She barely whispered the words she dreaded to speak. "I'm going to try my wings in the public defender's office the first of the year. I haven't made it official yet, but I know that they need me. It will mean my leaving the firm and taking a place in town with Jana."

His eyes held hers. "You've been thinking about this for a long time, haven't you?" She nodded. To her surprise, he continued, "Well, I've been thinking about it too. I've known your heart wasn't in your job with Martin. Your talents have been wasted there. You've grown into a remarkable woman, Melissa. I'm proud of you, and I'll be even more proud to see you busy helping people who need you.

"I've always known you and Jana wouldn't live here forever, sugar. It wouldn't be natural. I'm just sorry you're not leaving because you plan to bring some sharp young fellow into the family. If there's really no one in San Francisco, could that young D.A. be a likely prospect?"

Pain, as Brandon's face flashed across her mind's eye, combined with relief at Laurence's words.

"No, Dad." She shook her head. "I'm not interested in Darryl that way. But you don't feel I'm being disloyal by leaving you to start a life of my own?"

"Hell, no, Melissa!" His voice rose emphatically. "What have I done? Don't you feel you've got a life of your own, girl?"

Melissa turned from his puzzled gaze. "I'm so confused, Dad, I don't know what I know. I was so sure you'd object to our leaving, but I can see clearly now that I've imagined problems where there were none. It's just that I love you and I don't ever want to lose your love."

Strong arms reached out to cradle her. "You're not going to get rid of this old man that easily. I'm behind you, Melissa, one hundred percent, in anything you ever want to do. Hell, girl, you're my daughter! I don't ever want you to think of me as a stumbling block in the road to your future. There's an old Indian saying: 'To have, to hold, and in time, let go.' I guess that time has come for both of us.

"I thought a long time before I asked Irene to become my wife. I thought about you and Jana, mainly, and how it would affect you. But Irene's one in a million . . . like you. Once I was sure our marriage wouldn't jeopardize my relationship with you two girls, I decided to grab my happiness while I could. Do you think my getting married is disloyal to you and Jana?"

"No, of course not!" she denied honestly.

"I like to think neither time nor space could ever alter the love we share. We're family, Melissa. Family loyalty is like a sturdy oak tree. Have you ever wondered why the family is always characterized as a tree?" Not waiting for an answer, he continued. "A family is a tree. The strong trunk holds up the growing branches so that each can seek the sun in its own way. The roots go deep for nourishment and support, so that the branches can be free to climb into the sky." Melissa looked up into his eyes wonderingly. "You're free, sugar. The sky's the limit. My love will always support you."

Tears flowed freely down her cheeks. Laurence pulled an impeccable white linen handkerchief from his breast pocket to awkwardly dab at her wet eyes.

"Thank you, Dad, I can never tell you what this means to me." She almost sobbed.

Lightening the mood, he answered just as Irene returned to the room, "Come on now, Melissa. I want some more branches on this family tree while I'm still young enough to enjoy them. Don't be too quick to discount that young Jeffreys. He has a future in this state. He certainly meets with my approval."

Smiling through her tears, she took the handkerchief from him to finish the job. "I might try to oblige, Dad, if I could ever find anyone as suited to me as Irene is to you." Her heart cried silently: *Brandon, why couldn't it have been you?*

A worried frown that had furrowed Irene's smooth brow cleared as she tentatively approached them. Laurence reached out an arm and included her in his embrace.

"I've got another bottle of that bubbly stuff cooling," he smiled. "Let's all open it and really celebrate a new beginning for all the Bennetts." He winked down at the two women he held in his arms.

Wedding preparations added to the excitement of the holidays, making it a particularly busy time for the household. Melissa felt the fetters of her past loosen, replaced by a renewal of love for her father-in-law enhanced by her new sense of freedom.

Throughout these days of frenetic activity Melissa still found time to brood about Brandon. Thoughts of the scene she'd forced were so mortifying she could hardly bear to think of them. She flushed with anger at herself for being such a fool as to actually go to his apartment and invite upon herself the abuse he'd so aptly given. Any thoughts of his tenderness and charm were wiped away by the final and total humiliation she had felt upon finding herself outside his apartment with the door shut against her.

He'd made it clear there wouldn't be a second chance. Knowing she would never again love as she loved him, there were only two possibilities for her future life: either she wouldn't marry again or she would marry with only a part of herself, the greater share having been given to Brandon forever. Either way, she realized, complete happiness had been irrevocably denied her.

In the privacy of her room, when she had worn herself out

in regret over her decisions, she would weaken and take out her favorite photo of Brandon. Tears coursed down her cheeks unheeded as she raised the image of his handsome, vital face to her lips, but there was no comforting return of the love that she longed for.

Melissa had seen Darryl Jeffreys several times since her return. They found themselves at all the same parties—even paired by some hostesses who considered them a couple. Melissa sensed he knew she'd gone to San Francisco for reasons far more compelling than simply to visit Julia. He almost seemed relieved that she'd returned. His attentions were overly casual, as if he didn't want to scare her off.

Her feelings toward Darryl were ambivalent. On the one hand she felt that it would be unfair to marry him, knowing her feelings for Brandon would never abate. On the other, his devotion was such that letting him love her seemed to be enough for him. He didn't seem to need much response from her. But would things always be like that? As months and years wore on would he expect more than she would ever be able to give?

Abruptly, another brutal murder of a young woman occurred on the ski slopes, shaking the community to its foundations. Darryl's job consumed his time—there was no time for partying in the D.A.'s round-the-clock involvement. A little to her surprise, Melissa found herself missing his companionship—it was hard to be alone.

A feeling of fear gripped the community. Melissa read that the ski resorts were fast losing money since many winter sports enthusiasts were fearful of further attacks. There were many reported sightings of and supposed encounters with the murderer. People began looking with suspicion upon strangers—and indeed, upon anyone who was overtly friendly.

The discovery of the ravaged body of still another young woman on Christmas Eve shocked the citizenry into stark terror; it was now clear they had a psychopath in their midst. The district attorney's office was deluged with fervent demands that the murderer be apprehended and immediately brought to justice. Working through the holidays, they were swamped with still more witnesses who claimed that they had seen or been approached by the fiend. Each person was very carefully interviewed and a composite description of the suspect was being developed.

Although Laurence had shown a little reluctance when faced with the reality of Melissa's plans for her and Jana to move into town, he was now openly agreeable. Melissa knew the thought of her and Jana alone in the large secluded house while he and Irene were gone brought panic to his protective heart. The idea of her making the long drive back and forth at odd hours was also totally unacceptable to him. A Bennett-owned condominium was hastily furnished with the necessities and he made sure Melissa and Jana were safely moved before the wedding day. Unknown to Melissa, he arranged for around-the-clock protection for them.

The wedding provided a brief respite from the pall of apprehension that seized the city. Laurence and Irene decided not to postpone their honeymoon and departed, encouraged by Melissa's assurances that she and Jana would be cautious during their absence. Laurence had been firm in extracting a promise that they abstain from skiing altogether until a suspect had been apprehended, even though added security measures were being taken by the local police force to protect the ski slopes of the most popular resorts.

Late in January a young woman who had been accosted but had managed to break away from her attacker was brought in as an eyewitness to complete the composite drawing investigators had been working on. Her description led to the arrest of a part-time ski lift operator and ski school instructor, whose name was withheld pending further investigation. Melissa, along with the entire community, breathed a sigh of relief, hoping with his apprehension that the danger was over.

She was in her cramped cubicle at the public defender's office going over the evidence against an accused purse snatcher she'd been assigned to defend when a colleague stopped by with the news that the suspect's name had been released.

The color drained from her face. "Jason Leonard? There must be some mistake. Are you sure?"

"That's what I heard," the young attorney answered. "What's the matter? Do you know him?" But Melissa had grabbed her coat and was gone.

Reaching the D.A.'s office just as the handcuffed suspect was brought in under tight security for questioning, Melissa was shocked to recognize him. So it hadn't been a mistake, she thought with growing horror. Jason Leonard. She'd known him for several years. How many? Three? Four? She couldn't remember.

An especially friendly, easygoing young man, Jason was an excellent competition skier who supported his avid participation in the sport by working at the resort. They'd enjoyed a casual acquaintanceship—he'd been Jana's ski instructor from the start—and Melissa had skied with him several times during the past two or three years. Good company, he'd been a ski bum, one of many young skiers who take a year or more off between college and a business career to indulge themselves in their favorite sport.

Knowing these young men and women were often looked down upon by regularly employed ski enthusiasts who secretly envied their freedom to enjoy the slopes daily, Melissa wondered if some of this attitude had led to his arrest. Could this underlying antagonism be playing a part in the local residents' attitude in condemning this particular suspect?

But she had to admit his appearance did, more or less, fit the composite drawing the police had contrived, in that he was young, tall, and had long blond hair and light blue eyes in a rather thin face. The worried smile of recognition on that face as he passed by her imprinted itself upon her consciousness. He'd been such an excellent teacher—Jana'd learned to ski when little more than a toddler, and Jason Leonard had been the one who'd patiently taught her. There was no way Melissa could believe he was responsible for the murders.

At lunch with Darryl later that day she was highly agitated. Just how damning was the evidence against Jason Leonard? she wondered. After the waitress had taken their order of chef's salad and coffee, she felt moved to say, "Darryl, I know it isn't any of my business, but do you really think you have the right man in custody?"

"He was picked out of the lineup by that last girl who was assaulted and was fortunate enough to get away," he replied, a serious expression on his pleasant features.

"But isn't there a possibility she made a mistake? There are many young men who could fit that description. You looked a great deal like that yourself when you were younger," she argued.

"Melissa, this is a job for experts, not for suppositions. The whole town feels safer now that he's under arrest," he answered patiently.

"But what if he's not the right one? What if someone else did it?" she persisted.

"Don't worry, we still have plenty of security, and if he isn't guilty, maybe his arrest will flush out the real killer—if he's still out there.

"The Fur Rendezvous starts next week, and the promoters have been hounding our office for some action. At least this has quieted them down."

"Darryl, you don't mean he's been arrested to placate them, do you?" Shocked, her idealism was jolted to the core.

"Of course not," Darryl answered emphatically. "He fits the description and has been identified by an intended victim. That's pretty good evidence." His tone was uncharacteristically brusque.

"But you don't have anything concrete other than the

identification by a girl who could have been too hysterical to be accurate, do you?" she pressed.

"Not yet," he admitted, "but Leonard has no alibi for any of the times when the murders occurred, and he fits the description compiled from details given by several girls who believe they were approached. We're working hard on other leads to build an ironclad case against this guy."

"But I know him," Melissa argued plaintively. "He doesn't seem to fit the mold of a psycopath, as the papers have been calling him." Melissa persevered in spite of the trace of annoyance she could detect in Darryl's manner.

"How do you know him?" His eyes filled with curiosity.

"He's been Jana's ski instructor since she was three years old. And I've skied with him," she explained.

"I'd say you're a lucky woman to be sitting here, if that's the case. There haven't been any other murders or attempts on anyone's life since his arrest; that, along with a reliable intended victim's identification, satisfies most people as to his probable guilt."

"Darryl, he hasn't even been tried, much less convicted. How can you say that?" she asked accusingly.

"That's true. Thank you for reminding me of that fact. It's a point well taken," he said reasonably, choosing not to become perturbed at her criticism. "I solemnly promise you that I will do all in my power to see that he gets a fair, unbiased trial, but remember it's my job to build a case against him."

"Can you try to keep an open mind?" Melissa worried. "Will you pay as much attention to evidence that might clear him as to evidence that condemns him?"

"How can you ask that?" Darryl's voice was cold.

"I'm sorry," Melissa said. "It's just that his arraignment comes up soon, and in the middle of the Rondy people are more concerned with having fun than with tending to business."

"Well, I won't be one of them. Let's change the subject,

shall we? Are Laurence and Irene going to be back for the celebration?"

Melissa smiled and visibly relaxed thinking of them. "Laurence wouldn't miss it for anything. It's the only time he gambles and he does enjoy doing that, dressing up in turn-of-the-century garb and letting himself go. It seems uncharacteristic of him to enjoy gambling so much when he keeps such close supervision over the accounting department. He's the soul of generosity with his family, but he's cost-conscious with his company and his investors' money. I find it hard to reconcile his business approach to money with the unleashed enjoyment he finds at the blackjack tables."

Good humor restored, Darryl answered, "Well, I can reconcile it easily. The two go hand in hand. He could never have built Bennett Enterprises into what it is today if he weren't a superb gambler. I think he enjoys the Rendezvous so much because he can indulge himself freely in gambling without worrying about other people's money. The stakes are high, but I've heard he's rarely on the losing end."

"I'm sure you're right—that must account for it. Did I tell you I got a postcard from them?"

He shook his head, indicating his interest with an encouraging smile, obviously pleased he had chosen a distracting topic.

"They're in Sweden now. . . ."

The rest of their lunch passed in casual conversation about the upcoming Fur Rendezvous, the wintertime celebration of Alaska's frontier past. Darryl, a former dogsled racer, expressed his concern that the recently introduced two-hundred-mile cross-country snowmobile races were beginning to overshadow the traditional world champion dogsled event. The festivities were gaining both national and international reputation; consequently, all available hotel rooms had been booked solidly for months in advance.

"What are your plans, Melissa?" Darryl asked in a seemingly casual manner. "I've missed our dates. Would you like to come to the fur auction and the Miners' and Trappers' Costume Ball with me? I think I can fit that much free time into my schedule."

Melissa's heart sank. She didn't want to hurt this fine gentle man, but there was no way she could let him go on hoping. It was too cruel. She took a deep breath. "I'm sorry, Darryl. I just can't go with anyone this year. In fact, I think I should tell you . . ."

Darryl smoothly interrupted, as if knowing what she intended to say. "Well, if you have a change of heart, be sure and let me know."

A change of heart. If only he knew how ironic his words were. Dear God, if only it were possible, Melissa sighed.

Although she agreed to Darryl's request to drop the subject of the ski slope murderer, she wasn't mollified. Her heart went out to the young man in jail. She remembered Brandon intimating that women were too emotional to be good attorneys. Was there some truth in what he said? Was this the case with her? Was she letting her feelings sway her ability to judge the situation rationally? She didn't know. It was true that as the madcap days of the Rendezvous went by, there were no more incidents of the gruesome type the silent, glacial mountain had witnessed. Everywhere she went talk would turn to the murders, and she was torn apart by the vicious remarks and expressions of revenge that were directed against the mild-mannered young man locked up in jail. Learning from Darryl that Jason Leonard had been moved to solitary confinement to protect him from other prisoners, who were incensed by the nature of the crimes of which he'd been accused, Melissa became more disturbed, fearing for Leonard's safety as well as his state of mind.

On the gloomy gray morning of Leonard's arraignment, when he was at last formally charged with the murders, Melissa was in court having managed to secure a seat in the back row. The media were everywhere, attempting to get photos of the man as he shielded his face from exploding flashbulbs with handcuffed arms. Hostility heated the crowded courtroom. Melissa loosened the scarf at her neck, suffering from its suffocating intensity. Teeming crowds gathered in the corridors, loud voices and angered faces projecting a lynch mob mentality that was almost frightening.

When it was over, Melissa could stand it no longer: she felt compelled to let the accused man know that at least one person hadn't judged him without a trial. Without discussing her plans with anyone, she quietly made arrangements to visit him.

The uneasy interview took place in a partitioned, secured room—the prisoner on one side of the impenetrable divider, Melissa on the other. The conspicuous presence of an armed guard lent a sinister aspect to the meeting. Melissa's breath caught hurtfully in her chest when the door opened and Jason Leonard was led in. She was deeply distressed to see the young prisoner handcuffed and shackled, his warm tan fading to an unhealthy pallor, his hair hanging lank and neglected, his eyes holding the look of a beaten dog.

The few meaningless words of comfort that came to mind were met with absolute silence. Only when she asked if she could personally contact his family did he fleetingly raise his eyes to hers.

"I don't have any," was his terse reply.

Melissa asked softly, "Is there anyone else?"

"No. I've been on my own for a long time. Skiing's been my life." In the eyes that now candidly met hers for an instant Melissa saw a glimpse of the lighthearted fellow she'd known, picturing him patiently, kindly teaching her young daughter to ski. "I've followed the ski season from continent to continent. A little prize money, giving lessons, working lifts when I had to—anything to keep me going and out there on the slopes.

"I've never even been able to stand the thought of an indoor job." His eyes darted around the windowless room like a caged, frightened animal.

"You shouldn't be here, Mrs. Bennett," he said, lowering his voice to a near whisper. "You shouldn't have anything to do with me. I don't want any harm to come to you or Jana because of me. Nobody believes I'm innocent. They tell me everyone who's arrested says the same thing." He lifted his shoulders in a gesture of futility. "It's all like a bad dream. I keep thinking I'll wake up and find I've imagined the whole thing. I wish to hell they'd find that guy before he kills somebody else." He shook his unkempt head with a poignant sadness.

His words, coupled with the gesture, tore painfully at Melissa's conscience. She hadn't done enough. None of them had done enough. There wasn't one shred of evidence against Jason Leonard—outside of his identification by a terror-stricken girl—that might not be purely coincidental. She had to find a way to help him prove his innocence. She couldn't rest until she did.

"I'll find some way to help you," she promised, just before he was taken away. "Don't give up."

Left with the visual image of his eyes lighting with a look of guarded hope, Melissa sat for several minutes quietly considering her alternatives.

CHAPTER THIRTEEN

It had been a mistake to go to bed so ridiculously early, Melissa realized, as the noise of the celebrating city grated on her consciousness. What had made her think she could escape from her problems by piling into bed right after she'd tucked Jana in? Her thoughts would allow no sleep until she reached some sort of decision. What was she going to do to help Jason Leonard? Unless she came up with something, her visit would have harmed more than helped him by leaving the illusion of false hope.

The occasional rockets bursting in the night sky jarred her nerves unjustifiably. She glanced at the clock. It's blue-line numbers clearly proclaimed the time: 8:23. The last twenty-three minutes had seemed like hours! Acting without volition, she threw back the coverlet, swung her bare feet over the edge, and pushed them into comfortable fleece slippers before shrugging into a warm robe.

In the kitchen after pouring a glass of milk, she sat down at the dinette table, mulling over her disturbing thoughts. Though convinced of his innocence, she had no proof—certainly nothing that would convince a jury. She couldn't even serve as a character witness, her acquaintance with him was so slight. Yet the thought of an innocent man languishing in jail, the knowledge that an official accusation of the terrible murders had been made, and her fear that the real killer was still at large weighed heavily on her conscience.

Sipping the cool milk, she thought back. Memories of the

young skier, free and graceful on the pure white snow-covered slopes, contrasted with the sight of his wan, dejected, incarcerated figure, brought tears to her eyes. Getting up, she pulled a tissue from a box on the counter and blew her nose. She took a bottle of Kahlúa from a lower cupboard. Without measuring she stirred some of the warm brown liqueur into the milk.

She paced the floor, glass in hand, absorbed in thought. The trouble was she had no one to turn to for advice. Irene and Laurence, just returned from their honeymoon, were happily caught up in a mad social whirl during the festivities of the Rondy. No one else she knew would be interested in seriously discussing the possibility of Jason Leonard's innocence. People were too relieved to have someone behind bars, giving them substantial evidence that they need no longer fear for their safety, to even consider that he might be the wrong man. An intermittent spatter of firecrackers ignited by revelers broke through the steady city hum of the night, now just barely permeating her consciousness.

Sipping the coffee-colored drink, she remembered Darryl had been fairly patient when she'd questioned him about her concerns, but she knew it would be pushing her luck to try to pursue the topic any further with him. The whole case seemed hopeless, but her conscience continued to nag. Somehow she had to do something. But what?

As for the attorney who'd been appointed by the court, she thought with raised eyebrow, there would be little help coming from that source. He belonged in a classroom teaching the history and theory of law, not on the floor of a courtroom actively defending a client. His appearance was unimposing, his delivery anything but dynamic. As a result, his track record was appalling. No attorney in Anchorage would have less chance of freeing his client. It might have been nothing more than coincidence, but Melissa couldn't quite suppress the suspicion that the choice of this particular public defender had been deliberate. It seemed to support her contention that the skier had already been tried and found guilty even in the eyes of the most powerful, influential residents of Anchorage.

Returning to the kitchen, she poured a little more Kahlúa into her drink. There wasn't anything she could personally do for him—she was far too inexperienced to take on the case herself. But was she going to stand by and watch justice be reduced to a travesty? No, damn it! She was not!

Surely there had to be other avenues open to her. She sat down on the edge of the textured couch to once again think the matter through rationally. Hire another lawyer for him? At this late date, with public opinion running so high, it would be impossible to retain anyone in Anchorage. Accepting the case now would amount to career suicide for a prominent local attorney. She'd considered calling Professor Burke for a recommendation of someone from the lower forty-eight, until she'd remembered that he'd planned to take the winter term off to travel—she wouldn't be able to reach him.

Then there was Julia—she would surely know of someone. No, Melissa thought with a grimace, that was completely out of the question. There was little doubt whom Julia, ever the matchmaker, would recommend. Still . . .

Resuming her restless pacing, she fought an inner war. In her heart of hearts she'd known ever since this afternoon that there was only one man equal to the task—only one man with the expertise and eloquence to take on an entire city: Brandon Kade. The battle raged within her. Could she put her personal feelings aside and humble herself for a noble purpose?

Lord knows, she didn't want to ask him to take the case. Cheeks blazing hotly, she remembered his savage embrace and the door closed against her the last time they'd met. She cringed, remembering how foolishly she'd confessed her love, begging him to take her back.

The angry look on Brandon's strong face was etched

deeply, hurtfully, hauntingly on her mind. But there was a second haunting face that superseded it in her thoughts—that of the dejected suspect in the cold cell. A long string of firecrackers, sounding as if they had been set off in the parking lot of her building, exploded like supercharged popcorn, shaking her from her reverie.

Instinctively the mother in her turned toward Jana's room, quietly pushing open the door to see if the noise had disturbed her slumbering child. Relieved, she saw that Jana's small face was peaceful . . . even smiling. In an instant, the heartwarming sight brought back to Melissa all of her beautiful summer memories. Silently she admitted to herself that, second only to this child, loving Brandon had brought the greatest pleasure of her life. But it had left her the greatest pain.

In spite of herself, her mouth curved in a wistful smile, recalling the contented look she'd seen on Jana's face whenever Brandon had carried the sleeping child to bed. In fact, Jana'd always worn a smile whenever she'd been with Brandon. Moving to adjust the drapes, Melissa wondered: could Jana be dreaming of him? She had been thinking so hard about him herself . . . could her strongly charged feelings have transmitted an image of him to her little daughter? Their minds often did run on the same wavelength. If so, she was sure Jana's subconscious thoughts would not be tormented ones.

"Pleasant dreams, little one," she whispered, brushing the child's sweet forehead with a kiss. Softly shutting the door, she made up her mind. She had to call for Brandon's help.

Starting for the phone, Melissa stopped dead in her tracks, assailed by another fear. Egotist that he was, wouldn't Brandon think her request merely a ploy to enable her to see him again? Would he take her concern seriously? Chilling thoughts of the murderer, loose somewhere in the throngs that filled the streets and hotels, or perhaps still on the mountain mingling among the confident skiers, filled her heart with fear. At this moment the monster might be readying himself to strike again at some unsuspecting, trusting young woman. Could she honestly let personal pride stand in the way of doing the right thing? Could she accept the responsibility if another victim died because of her inaction?

She checked her watch. Nine o'clock. It would be eleven in San Francisco. Was it too late to call? No, Brandon rarely went to bed before midnight. Besides, if she called him at home, there was no way he could refuse the call. At the office his secretary might serve as a buffer if he didn't want to speak to her. She couldn't risk that.

Driven by intense dread, she picked up the phone and dialed Brandon's private number. With the sound of the first ring her courage diminished. Tempted to hang up . . .

"Hello," the husky, resonant voice answered, sounding instantly alert.

"Brandon . . . this is Melissa," she stammered, trying to control her trembling voice. Dead silence met her announcement. Could she go on with this? she wondered, barely stopping herself from slamming down the receiver. But impelled by the unwanted thrill of knowing they were linked together at least for a moment by the phone lines, she slowly drew it back to her ear.

Finally he said, "Yes, Melissa, what is it?"

"Brandon—" She paused, tongue-tied. Then, heartened by the fact that he was even willing to continue the conversation, she hurried on nervously, "This is strictly a business call."

"A business call?" Incredulity filled his voice. "From Alaska? At eleven o'clock at night? Why didn't you call my office in the morning?"

"Some things just can't wait. Believe me, I wouldn't have called you if there had been anyone else who could help."

"I can well believe that." He laughed outright.

"Well, it's true!" she shot back indignantly.

"What's the matter, Snowbird? Are you in jail?" His manner was humorously patronizing.

"No, damn it, but I'm afraid an innocent man is," she retorted hotly. Same old Brandon!

"Are you talking about your ski slope murderer, by any chance?"

"Yes." Trust him to be up on everything, she thought with grudging respect. "Brandon, I want to hire you to defend him." As the words left her mouth she realized she hadn't even considered how Darryl would react to her interference. But she couldn't let herself worry about that now.

"Why me? Don't you have any practicing attorneys in Anchorage?"

Mildly encouraged by this humorous wisecrack, combined with his air of familiarity and seeming lack of hostility, she continued. "Brandon, he's innocent. I feel sure of it, and that means the real murderer is still out there loose somewhere."

"What makes you think I'd take this case? I don't take every case some beautiful woman with sapphire eyes calls me about in the middle of the night, just because her intuition tells her a suspect is innocent," he teased. "Who is the prisoner, anyhow? Some creepy little nobody?"

"Forget I called!" Nerves frayed to the breaking point, Melissa shouted into the phone. "My sapphire eyes, as you call them, have nothing whatsoever to do with this! I was a fool to contact you. I forgot: you're only interested in two things: sex and socially prominent people," she spat out disdainfully. "Well, I'm sorry, but his name's definitely not in the social register."

"Now calm down, Melissa," Brandon chuckled. Soothingly, as if talking to a child, he asked, "What makes you think he's innocent?"

Fighting back tears of rage, Melissa debated with herself. This conversation was being carried on on two levels, there was no doubt about it. There was an undercurrent of emotion on Brandon's part; she knew him too well—she could feel it. Something primitive forced her to respond to his question. "I went to the jail and had a long talk with him today. And besides, I know him."

"How do you know him?" A sudden sharp edge to Brandon's voice carried distinctly on the line.

"He was Jana's ski instructor and I've skied with him a number of times," she replied evenly.

"If I agree to come, will you promise to stay away from the jail until after I've seen and talked with him?" Brandon demanded, forged steel in his voice.

"Yes," she meekly agreed, surprised at his unaccountable vehemence.

"All right. I'll be there on the first flight I can catch. What concerns me far more than defending your little jailbird is your fear that the killer is still loose. There happen to be other aspects of this case that interest me too," he offered without explanation. Relaxing into a drawl, he went on, "Besides, the Fur Rendezvous and the chance to see Jana would be enough to tempt me to come right now."

"Thank you, Brandon." She let out a relieved sigh.

"You're welcome, Melissa." He was almost civil, she thought, as he hung up.

Was it possible he was coming? she wondered as she put down the phone. Was it her imagination or had his voice sounded genuinely friendly at times? Could they be friends? She couldn't allow herself to hope for more. If he did decide to take the case it would be a business arrangement between them. Strictly business. Heart sinking, she remembered his words: it was Jana he'd said he'd like to see.

Brandon was coming. That was all that mattered. Finishing off her drink in a swallow, she placed the glass on the coffee table before exhaustedly collapsing on the couch. Emotionally draining though it had been to talk with him, a surge of excitement warmed her blood as the sound of his voice reverberated repeatedly in her brain. Lord, how she loved that man. Every fiber in her body incessantly yearned for him; she knew the torment of loving him would never stop.

Why was he coming so quickly in response to her call? Usually, before he decided to even consider a case he'd send an investigating team ahead. After all, his services were in great demand—she'd never known him to be between cases; on the contrary, he was always embroiled in two or three at a time. *Why was he dropping everything to come himself?*

In San Francisco there would be no sleep for Brandon Kade that night. After replacing the receiver in its cradle, he reached up to click on his brass bedside lamp, pulling the pillows together so that he half sat, propped against the solid oak headboard of his massive bed. He'd barely flipped the switch off when the phone had rung. Flinging muscular bare arms on the top of his head, grasping a wrist with one hand, he let a broad smile spread across the features of his handsome face. Melissa had called him! She needed him! What more could he ask? And she still cared for him! He knew it! Damn it, he could feel it in his bones. His arm actually tingled from holding the phone, he realized, rubbing and then smoothing the black hair on his forearm. Or was it his imagination? Could the sensation be caused simply by the sophomoric thrill of hearing her familiar voice again?

Elated, he thought of the airline ticket for Anchorage he'd purchased days ago lying conspicuously on the dresser next to his billfold and jewelry. The luck of the Irish, his dad would have called it, he remembered fondly. Like a bolt out of the blue, Melissa's late-night plea for help had solved what had seemed like an insurmountable problem.

Brow furrowed, he remembered the long stormy weeks of indecision he'd suffered through. It hadn't escaped his notice that his employees and even his associates had begun to avoid him, not wishing to risk an encounter while he'd been in the pits of depression. Finally there'd been no way around the inescapable conclusion: he wanted that woman—Melissa Collins Bennett was the only one he wanted.

Having made up his mind to go to Melissa, he'd been grateful that the name Brandon Kade carried enough weight to get him an airline ticket and a suite in the overbooked city. The one stumbling block left to overcome had been how to approach her once he'd arrived. He'd considered calling to say he was coming to take Jana on the long promised ski trip, but after the episode at his apartment he'd been afraid Melissa would have turned that idea down flat. Anyway, he couldn't afford to take the chance. He would have had to appear on her doorstep, walking into Lord knows what.

He'd thought of asking Julia about Melissa's romantic status more than once in the past few days, but there was no way he could humble himself that far. His eyes glanced at the packed bags on the floor and slid toward the new cross-country skis and poles standing against the arm of his chair. His smile grew and burst into an audible chuckle. The guise of coming to the Rondy had finally been the solution he'd come up with, but Melissa had made his intended arrival and reentry into her life so much easier. No matter what rivals he might find, he would make short shrift of them. He'd already screwed up, wasting too much time he could have spent with Melissa.

The past few months had not been easy. The traditional Christmas spent with the Raymonds had been the worst. It hadn't been fun watching the newlyweds, Julia and Scott, basking in glowing happiness. At times it had almost been too much for him: he'd taken to drinking a lot more eggnog than usual. Even Grace had frowned at the way he'd liberally stiffened his drinks with extra brandy. But there'd just been too many memories of Melissa haunting him everywhere he'd turned. He'd had to blot them out somehow.

And Julia—he snorted, remembering—had been downright cool, almost obnoxious in her thinly veiled hostility toward him. Purposely he'd avoided her, not wanting to get into an argument about Melissa, which Julia's burning eyes had warned him she was spoiling for.

Pulling his arms down, he rubbed his hands over the coarse stubble on his cleft chin, remembering. One thing the whole episode at Christmas had brought home to him was that he did need family. The Raymonds were his family—had been for years, though he'd never really thought of them in those terms. He'd found their disapproval hard to take.

Leaving La Jolla for Acapulco earlier than he'd planned, he'd found no solace on the warm beaches there either. Bittersweet memories of Melissa and Jana intruded, making it impossible to even enjoy his favorite Mexican foods. Every bite he'd put into his mouth tasted like sawdust.

When he'd faced the issue squarely and finally confessed to himself that he couldn't live without Melissa, he'd begun making plans. The intended trip to Anchorage was the outcome of much soul-searching, followed by decisive action. He was now ready to spend as much time as he needed to convince the little blonde that he loved her dearly, without reservations, and that whatever it took to make her happy was all right with him, so long as he could be any part of her life.

He'd continued to play a role with her, having been caught off guard by her unexpected call. A flood of things he'd wanted to say had risen to mind at the sound of her sweet voice—even speeches he'd been preparing. But he hadn't been able to voice a word of it, not wanting to give her a chance to reject his overtures on the phone. How could she be expected to know or believe what a changed man he was from the one she'd known? A telephone conversation was not the medium to use to convince a woman of the reality of your love. One thing he'd learned in the courtroom was to hold your cards close until it was time to show them. He had to be patient just a little longer.

Still so idealistic! He shook his head, a smile twisting the corner of his mouth, as he thought over what she'd said. He'd had to be firm with her—anything to extract a promise that she'd stay away from Jason Leonard. He hadn't drawn an easy breath until he'd heard the man was behind bars. He'd been chafing at the bit to get up there as added reports concerning the murders in Alaska had come in over the wire service. Unable to keep his mind from straying to that case, he'd gone over and over the considerable dossiers he'd compiled on similar cases.

Thank God, Melissa hadn't been one of the victims. Actually, when he had thought she might be in some kind of danger, the whole situation between them had become clear—so crystal clear. It had been then that he'd known she meant everything to him.

So she wanted to hire him, did she? Well, she was going to get more than she bargained for. Strictly business, she'd said. He grinned. She didn't know yet what kind of business *he* had in mind. Speaking of business, he had a few last-minute details to take care of. Too excited to sleep, he bounded naked from his bed, crossed the room, and stepped into the shower, from where his rich baritone voice echoed with happy song.

Close to five the following afternoon, after what had seemed an eternity of waiting, Brandon finally called from his hotel and asked her to meet him for a drink. Melissa wondered how he'd secured a room in the best hotel the city had to offer on such short notice. She knew all available rooms had been booked months in advance for the last three days of the Fur Rendezvous. Someone must have canceled their reservations, she thought; or was the celebrity attorney's influence great enough to take precedence over the many influential people who were vying for rooms in the crowded city? Fortunately with the town celebrating so vigorously she was sure his presence would be taken for granted and not be linked with the case, even by the people who would recognize him.

She'd spent the afternoon indecisively searching through her wardrobe for a proper outfit to wear. The tailored business suits she'd acquired would look hopelessly out of place in the gala crowd at the fashionable hotel. A good dress with a string of pearls might make him think she expected to be invited to dinner, and she certainly didn't want to give that impression.

After putting on and taking off practically everything she owned, one outfit still hung in her closet untouched . . . one that she hadn't thought she'd ever wear again . . . the one she'd been wearing when Brandon Kade had first kissed her. Something compelled her to take it from the hanger. Although lightweight for the season, with navy boots and her silver ranch mink coat it would be fine.

Smoothing the fine wool skirt over her hips, she remembered the feel of Brandon's hands on her body. An undeniable shiver of anticipation prickled down her spine as she gave her hair a final brush before picking up her navy handbag and rushing out the door.

Driving to the hotel along the crowded snow-covered streets, Melissa took deep breaths, forcing herself to remain calm. Her efforts did nothing to slow the rapid beating of her heart; in her nervousness she turned up the radio to drown out the sound of its throb and that of the pulse racing in her ears.

Knees shaking—was it from cold or emotion?—she walked into the lobby and immediately saw his tall, dark figure standing near the front desk, head and shoulders above everyone else in the room. Rooted to the carpet, she watched his face light up in a charming smile as he caught sight of her and then threaded his way toward her. The powerful shock of seeing him caused a sudden, momentary paralysis to grip her body.

He looked thinner, she noticed, and though smiling, his

face appeared a little older, as if he'd been through a major ordeal. She felt an insane desire to throw herself into his arms and kiss away the worry lines between his eyes. Unable to take another step, she tried to smile in return, but her face felt stiff as she made an effort to restrain the rush of emotions that weakened her body.

Their eyes met, locked in greeting as he gazed down at her. For a brief instant she felt there were only the two of them left in the room. Slowly sounds around them intruded into her consciousness; she blinked, and the moment was over. Allowing herself to be guided, his body slightly in front of hers as he protectively maneuvered her through the crowd toward the cocktail lounge, she was glad they were quickly seated at a small table or her knees might have given way beneath her altogether.

Practice a little self-discipline, she told herself sternly. This is business, remember? You're nothing more than a client securing the services of an attorney. But her traitorous heart asked, how is it possible to be businesslike when your attorney is the most attractive man on the planet and all you can think of is being in his arms with his mouth on yours?

"Thank you for coming so quickly," she said after they'd both somewhat nervously ordered white wine.

"My pleasure," Brandon responded in his maddening drawl, still smiling devastatingly, his intense eyes holding hers with an allure unweakened by the past long months of separation and recrimination.

"How've you been, Melissa?" He slowly took in the ink-navy suit as she pushed the mink back from her shoulders. His gray-blue eyes clearly told her he remembered when she'd last worn that outfit. Leaning forward, resting his elbows on the small table between them, he went on, "I've been thinking a great deal about you."

Ridiculously, she fought back the impulse to ask him just what he'd been thinking. "I've been just fine, thank you," she lied.

The charged silence grew heavy, fraught with emotion. Dear Lord, how am I ever going to get through this? It was worse even than she'd imagined it would be. She ached everywhere with an excruciating pain, as if all her wounds were being torn open.

She'd have to let his remark pass, however beguiling his intended meaning was to her heart, though she knew it would have taken days to tell him of the hours she'd spent thinking of him. She couldn't stand to have the conversation get onto a personal level.

After several moments lost in wonder staring at the reality of his face so tantalizingly close to hers, she tore her eyes from his and shook her head slightly. Distractedly, she began to search her handbag in the dim light of the booth for the sheet of paper on which she had listed names, addresses, and other pertinent information about the case she thought he might need. Acutely conscious that his eyes followed her every movement, she nervously fumbled through everything in her bag before she found it. Silently she held it out toward him with a shaking hand; he took it as if they needed to speak no words in order to understand each other, his strong hand brushing hers, sending sparks of electricity along the nervepaths of her senses.

"About your retainer," she blurted out.

He leaned closer, that particularly devilish look in his eyes she remembered only too well. "It might be far more than you're willing to pay."

Fingering the stem of her glass, her hand shaking so violently she feared he would notice, she knew she couldn't lift the goblet to her lips. Could she take his words at face value, or was there an innuendo hidden among them?

He straightened up and leaned back casually. "We won't worry about that part just yet," he remarked, an enigmatic smile lifting his lips. "I'll get right on the case," he assured her, suddenly the professional as he placed the folded paper in the pocket of his jacket.

"How long are you going to be in Alaska?" Her voice sounded high to her ears. She held her breath, inwardly praying he'd stay at least long enough to give the case serious consideration . . . and . . . and . . . ? Well she knew, just having him near was an agony so sweet she couldn't bear to face the bleak emptiness she knew would engulf her once he was gone . . . gone out of her life.

"That depends . . . on you." He sounded almost wistful, a note in his voice rare to his speech.

On me? she thought. When have I ever had any control over him or his actions? She nodded toward the paper in his pocket, wanting to divert herself from puzzling over the enigmatic remark.

"Darryl Jeffreys is the district attorney," she explained. "He's a good friend of mine. I haven't told him that I called you. Please don't mention my name to him. Oh, and something you may not know: I've been working for the public defender's office since the first of the year." She offered the information falteringly.

"You're not working for your father-in-law any longer?" Brandon asked with surprise.

"No. I wasn't happy in civil law, and Darryl suggested I take a different job. Actually he wanted me to work for him, but I didn't want to get into prosecution, so I took a position with the public defender. Dad really didn't need me in the corporation," she admitted. "Darryl helped me see that."

Oh, forget it, she told herself. With every word that comes out of your mouth you're only making matters worse. She'd hoped Brandon wouldn't get the idea that she and Darryl were anything more than business colleagues, but the way she'd botched up her explanation of the situation between them, trying needlessly to expand upon it, had made her relationship with the D.A. sound ambiguous even to her ears. Damn it! Why had she felt the need to explain and justify her relationship with Darryl? Why had she just assumed Brandon might read something sexual into it? Why had she doubted that he would see it as anything more than purely professional?

Brandon's face clouded. Looking down, he swirled the wine in his glass with a fluid movement of his strong wrist. Watching a small muscle working at the corner of his square jaw, she could see that he was clearly annoyed with her. She couldn't blame him. It was as he had said long ago: women couldn't control their emotions, and she was certainly living proof of that condemnation tonight. She could imagine what her face looked like at the moment—a love-sick sophomore sentimentally staring at the unattainable captain of the football team.

I can't take this, she thought with rising panic. One faux pas after another! How many will I make if I continue this conversation any longer?

Please legs, hold out . . . long enough to get me out of here before turning to useless jelly. Before she left there was one more thing she had to say.

"Brandon," she managed softly.

"Yes . . . what is it?" He lifted his eyes to her face again.

The impact of his gaze was physical, causing her breath to catch in her throat. She forced out the words, not wanting to bring the hateful scene back to mind, yet compelled to say them. "I want to apologize for hitting you. I've never done anything like that before to anyone. Please understand, I'm truly sorry."

"I deserved it. Let's forget it," he answered, his face hardening, as though it were something he did not wish to be reminded of.

If he wasn't still angry, how could she account for the puzzling look that came over his face during this exchange? She realized with a sigh that she couldn't read his feelings at all.

When she rose from the small table, Brandon stood, too, looking down at her. Hesitantly she offered her hand in farewell. He took it and held it for a long moment, almost as if he were undecided as to what to do next.

"I've got plans for the evening," he told her evenly, "but I'll get back to you as soon as I can."

At his words she jerked her hand from his, face flaming. Naïvely, she'd just assumed he'd come alone. Could it be there was another woman waiting for him even as they'd talked? Of course, he'd said he'd come to have fun at the Rondy. The blood left her face as suddenly as it had come. Pale as ice, Melissa turned on her heel without another word and walked quickly from the room, her heart beating wildly.

What did I say now? the tall man wondered, shaking his head in amazement as he stood watching the petite blonde's hasty retreat from the lounge.

CHAPTER FOURTEEN

After snacking dispiritedly on an apple and Havarti, Melissa dozed fitfully on the couch awaiting Jana's return from a day spent with her grandparents. A key turning in the lock awakened her around ten.

Jana bounded in the door like an eager puppy followed closely by her grandfather. Eyes sparkling, she bounced down on the couch as she snatched off her hat and pulled her hands from warm mittens. "It's snowing, Mommy! It's snowing! It's been so long since we've gone, can we go skiing tomorrow?" she pleaded appealingly.

"*May* we go skiing," Melissa corrected, straightening to a sitting position and smoothing down the back of her hair. "What do you think, Dad? Do you think it would be safe?"

"I'm sure it would be perfectly all right for the two of you to go skiing," he answered reassuringly. "My only worries are about icy road conditions. Will you give me a call when you get home?"

"Of course I will." It would be better to get out of town for the day than to sit around at home waiting for a call that might never come.

"Yes, to answer your question, honey, we may go. It's a terrific idea. I'm glad you thought of it." Melissa reached out and pulled Jana close, nuzzling the child's cool face against her own warm one, before impulsively enveloping her daughter in an unusually strong hug.

Struggling free, Jana looked at her mother in surprise. "Have you been crying, Mommy? Your face looks funny."

Touching her tearstained cheeks, Melissa realized she must have been crying in her sleep. "No, dear. I've been sleeping. In fact I just woke up when I heard you come in. I'm fine . . . really." She added cheerfully, "How are you?" Her arm encircled the child gently, drawing her close again. "Did you have a good day? As if I need to ask."

Laurence looked at her appraisingly. Though she might have convinced Jana, Melissa knew that she hadn't convinced him. To avoid any questions he might pose, she hastily suggested, "Would you mind seeing yourself out, Dad? If we're going skiing we'll have to get to bed early—like right now!" She gave Jana a light, teasing pat on the bottom.

"Sure, sugar." Laurence's eyes narrowed as he observed her keenly. "But if anything's bothering you, you know you can call me anytime. Night or day. And remember, it's never too late to change your mind about going to the costume party at the club. I've got two strong arms, and I'd like nothing better than to enter that room with a beautiful woman on each of them."

Touched, fighting back tears that threatened to spill, Melissa nodded mutely in thanks, appreciating his understanding.

While dressing for bed Jana prattled gaily about her day spent viewing the children's dogsled races from a tethered, colorfully striped hot-air balloon. Melissa half listened, preoccupied by the guilt she felt over not telling Jana that Brandon was in Anchorage. Somehow she just couldn't bring herself to share the news, even though she knew Jana would be delighted. It wouldn't be fair. The way things stood between herself and Brandon it might be best for the little girl if she never saw her "uncle" again.

After tucking her daughter in, Melissa returned to the living room, now wide awake. She glanced at her watch. It was ten twenty. It would be ten twenty-one, then ten twenty-two, then ten twenty-three . . . over and over again for the rest of her life—the life she would live without the love she knew she could share with only one man. Arms crossed, she stared at the silent phone, wishing that it would ring but knowing that it would not.

With a strange sense of unreality, she heard it ring as she stood fixedly staring down at it. Its shrill voice sounded a sure-to-be false promise. She let it ring several times before reaching out to still its clamor.

Her voice listless, lifeless, she answered, "Hello."

"I went to see your jailbird friend," the deep voice of Brandon Kade began without preamble. "Spent over three hours talking with him. Interesting specimen, I must say."

"Well, what do you think? Is it too soon for you to have an opinion as to whether you'll take the case?" Melissa responded evenly without missing a beat, though her thoughts ricocheted madly. So he'd spent at least part of the evening working. The heavy load her heart carried lightened just a fraction.

"I've still got a number of things to check out. I'll be up for a good part of the night. Meant to get back to you earlier, but it took much longer to interview Jason Leonard than I'd anticipated. Fascinating fellow." His speech was clipped, professional.

Abruptly Brandon shifted gears, relaxing into a drawl. "I know it's too late to speak to Jana, but will you tell her, the minute she opens those baby blue eyes, that her Uncle Brandon is ready to start those cross-country lessons she promised whenever she has any free time?"

"Actually, we're planning to ski tomorrow." The words seemed to slip out of their own volition as Melissa unconsciously twisted and straightened the coiled phone cord between her fingers.

"Okay. What time are you picking me up?" he asked matter-of-factly.

Taken aback, Melissa stammered. "My car's quite small.

It's a squeeze with all our equipment for two adults and Jana."

"Who else is going?" Brandon demanded.

"No one. Just Jana and me."

"Then what's the problem?"

A long silence followed.

"Melissa, are you still there?"

Squaring her slight chin and resolutely taking a breath, she blurted out what had been foremost in her mind all evening. "Didn't you come to Anchorage with someone else?" A little green devil prompted her to add, "What's she going to do all day?"

"She? Who in the hell are you talking about? I'm not here with anyone. What ever gave you that idea?"

Her hand shot briefly over the mouthpiece as she let out an audible sigh of relief. Her emotions had played havoc with her good sense, she realized. But why couldn't he simply have told her he intended to start work on the case this evening instead of leaving her to stew over groundless fears of another woman being with him?

"Oh, it was just something you said. Never mind, it's not important anymore," she voiced coolly. "We'll be there about eight thirty. How's that? Too early?"

"No, it'll be fine."

"Brandon"—her voice softened—"thank you. Jana'll be delighted to see you."

Responding to the warmth in her voice, he said "Good night, Melissa" in a tone that sounded to her ears like a seductive caress. The connection between them broke.

Rubbing her eyes and blinking from the light, Jana came padding into the room while Melissa was still holding the receiver against her cheek.

"I heard you talking, Mommy, and I couldn't sleep. Who called?"

Replacing the phone, Melissa put her arm around the little shoulders, steering the child back toward the bedroom door. Now she could be told.

"You've got a big day ahead of you tomorrow, baby—bigger than you thought. Uncle Brandon's here and he's ready for his ski lessons." The words, barely out of her mouth, were greeted with Jana's enthusiastic response.

"Oh, goody! I knew he'd come!"

As she bent down to kiss the fine hair on her daughter's head, Melissa silently admitted she hadn't been half so sure herself.

In the early morning's darkness, Melissa dressed carefully in her favorite ski outfit—slim-fitting, aqua bib pants and a soft cashmere sweater of a lighter hue. After she was completely ready she woke her little daughter and quickly helped her dress. Donning a matching parka, Melissa drew on gloves of the same shade and stuffed her ski hat into her pocket before going out to load and warm up the car.

Putting Jana's cross-country skis on the rack was easy, but she hesitated, filled with uncertainty, as she stared at her own two sets. Downhill . . . or cross-country? Tempted to take the cross-countries, tempted to act as though she took it for granted Brandon meant to include her in his day, she found her hand reaching for the narrow wooden-laminate skis. But she stopped herself. She had too much pride to go where she wasn't invited.

But was it safe to ski the slopes? With Jason Leonard behind bars the whole town seemed to think so, she thought in disgust. Darryl certainly did—even Laurence. Besides, all the murders had occurred in the evening. She would be safe if she stayed on the crowded well-used runs. She picked up her new downhill set, regrettably convinced that Brandon would prefer to spend the day alone with Jana.

Driving through the snow-covered streets, Melissa began to catch some of Jana's highly contagious excitement. Although she told herself it was unreasonable, she looked forward to the day with a greater sense of expectancy than any other in recent memory. When would Brandon's presence cease to be a necessary ingredient for her happiness? she wondered hopelessly.

As they drove up to the hotel, Brandon, clad in corduroy knickers and a heavy Scandinavian sweater, promptly came out carrying a new pair of slim skis and a satchel of gear. Melissa's breath caught in her throat at the sight.

"Hi, sweetheart! How's my girl?" Opening the passenger door, he greeted Jana, who almost choked him with a possessive hug given from her perch in the backseat. His spontaneous warmth equaled the child's as he returned her embrace.

"Good morning." He greeted her with a broad smile over Jana's shoulder.

"Good morning." Her tentative smile answered his.

Momentarily surprised to see him properly outfitted and attired for a sport he claimed he'd never tried, she reasoned that he'd probably had the necessary items sent over from the local ski shop the night before. I should have known Brandon Kade would never be caught wearing a makeshift outfit for anything, she mused.

"You'll need the key for the rack and the trunk," she offered. "Do you want any help?"

"No, thanks, I can manage." He smiled. "You stay put in where it's warm."

After competently mounting the skis on the rack and placing his new ski shoes and bag in the trunk, he opened the driver's door. Jingling the keys, he announced, "I'll drive."

It seemed so natural, so right to let him, that Melissa scooted over to the other bucket seat of her little black sports car without protest as they set out on the forty-mile trip.

"Uncle Brandon, I didn't know you knew how to cross-country ski. I thought I was going to teach you!" Jana complained petulantly from the backseat.

"I don't, and you are," he replied good-naturedly over his shoulder.

"But you have your skis and everything. I thought you'd have to rent some." Her statement was a question.

"I bought these a long time ago getting ready for this day," he answered. Gray-blue eyes caught Melissa's and held them meaningfully. Was he telling the truth? she wondered. Had he really meant to come in spite of everything that had gone wrong between them? Her mind swirled, unable to absorb the implications of that possibility.

When they came to a fork in the road, he asked, "Which way? Remember, I don't know how to get where we're going." Adding dryly, "It seems I never have. *Where are we going, Melissa?*"

"Oh . . . to the left," she answered quickly, feeling like a fool. Taken back by his surprising answer to Jana, she hadn't even remembered he wouldn't know which turns to make. But what did he mean by his last remark? Somehow she knew it had nothing to do with road directions.

But she had no time to mull it all over. On the drive up to the resort Brandon actively interrogated her about the ski slope murder case. As she talked with him, trying hard to respond to his incisively probing questions, Melissa realized she actually knew very little beyond what she'd read in the papers, like everyone else. Since she hadn't been assigned to the case at the office, the only additional knowledge she had stemmed from her slight acquaintance with the accused.

"Do you think he could be innocent?" she ventured to ask, when Brandon had at last finished questioning her.

"What I think isn't important," he answered, somewhat sharply. "Cases are built on facts, not suppositions." Melissa recalled Darryl saying almost the same thing. "I really can't go into the details right now"—he shifted his eyes to indicate Jana—"and I hate to tell you this—but you're going to be very disappointed with what I've learned." His eyes seemed to be offering consolation.

Melissa's hand stifled a sharp painful gasp. So it was Jason Leonard. Remembering her talk with him, she wondered briefly if he were a pathological liar, or if when he committed the unspeakable acts a part of him was in control that the other, decent side of him refused to acknowledge. Experiencing a nauseating, sinking feeling, she knew that Brandon's opinion was almost certainly accurate. It was far more important to her than Darryl's could ever be.

Brandon's mere physical presence had an effect on her like no other man's had ever had . . . or would ever have. She knew, too, with sudden clarity, that she would have to face the reality of Darryl's continuing romantic interest in her as soon as this whole episode was past.

She had to be honest with Darryl: there could never be anything between them—there was nothing left to give. Every fiber of her being belonged to Brandon, and always would, no matter how far-reaching or final their ultimate separation. As she looked sideways at his handsome profile with its strong jaw and well-formed features, she silently grieved for what might have been, had he, or she, or the circumstances of their lives been different.

Arriving at the alpinelike resort, tucked in the folds of the rocky prominence, they pulled on parkas for the brisk walk over crunchy packed snow to a cozy restaurant housed in a large half-timbered chalet. Jana chatted while they ate a fortifying brunch, filling Brandon in on the happenings of her life since they'd last been together. With a twinge of motherly pain, Melissa noticed how animated and eager her daughter was, how hard she tried to hold Brandon's unflagging attention.

Seeing Jana in this new light, she began to worry. Could she have been wrong? Did Jana actually expect more from Brandon than he had offered? Did she in truth, perhaps even unknowingly, look upon him as a substitute father? Anguish, heartbreaking in intensity, flooded over her at this possibility. Though Brandon's attachment to her daughter was genuine, Jana was doomed to disappointment if she expected a life with the three of them together.

Watching the two, Melissa felt sure her decision to bring her downhill equipment had been the right one. This way Brandon and Jana would be free to enjoy their short time alone together. Although things had gone smoothly so far, the ever-present undercurrent of tension between her and Brandon was so great that she suspected, before the day was over, it might have an adverse effect on her sensitive little daughter's spirit. Besides, she really wanted to be alone. Perhaps alone on the slopes she could come to grips with the devastating news concerning Jason Leonard—put to rest her emotional involvement.

Outside the chalet after they'd buckled on their skis, Melissa handed Brandon and Jana each a packet of raisins and nuts. She arranged a cocoa-filled flask around Jana's neck and handed Brandon a flask filled with coffee. With a twinkle in his eye he ignored her outstretched hand and bent low like an obedient child to allow her to arrange his flask as she had arranged Jana's. Uncomfortable, Melissa took care not to touch the jet black hair—hair that her hands longed to stroke—as she quickly reached around his neck and dropped the flask into place.

Taking a last look in the trunk, Brandon asked quizzically, "Where's yours?"

"I didn't bring anything for myself. I won't need it," she answered, slamming the lid shut, evading his eyes.

"Aren't you going with us?" he asked in surprise.

"I have new downhill skis, and with everything that's happened I haven't had a chance to try them out this season. Since Jana's going with you, I thought this would be a good chance for me to break them in." Her even tone belied the slight trembling of her body as she nervously pushed a stray lock of hair back under her soft knit hat.

"I'm disappointed," he said quietly. "Next time let's get together on this." Steel-blue eyes bored into hers.

Melissa felt a momentary twinge of regret that she hadn't planned to go with them. In a quandary over his true feelings, she almost felt guilty that she'd somehow let him down. Tears stung just below the eyelids. I've been crying ever since he came, she remembered unhappily—even in my sleep. Why am I making such a big deal over this? she wondered in amazement. He's just being polite, probably experiencing inward relief rather than disappointment, she thought with a trace of bitterness . . . although, looking at him again, she couldn't be sure.

After walking along to the start of Jana's favorite cross-country trail, Melissa said good-bye to them both. Anxious to be off, Jana didn't notice the lonely pensive look that came over her mother's face at the moment of their departure. Brandon gave her one quick, penetrating glance over his shoulder before the trail turned and they were lost from sight, but Melissa managed what she hoped was a cheerful smile and a small wave.

As she carried her skis to the slopes, the mood of elation she'd felt early that morning had completely evaporated. She didn't notice the rosy pink top of the mountain still visible through the low-hanging ominous clouds that threatened to obscure its presence. The sun was shining here and there on the slopes, filtering through the cloud cover, causing favored patches of snow to sparkle and glisten like hoards of diamonds. Taking a deep breath of the cold clear air, she started toward the nearest lift.

Riding up the first chair, her mind turned from unbidden mental pictures of Brandon and the way his athletic body had moved so surefootedly on the trail to thoughts of the young man in jail. She remembered him well on these very slopes. If Brandon was right, and she felt sure he must be,

Jason Leonard would never ski here again. The hills seemed so pure in their icy pristine whiteness, it was impossible to think of the demonic evil of a murderer, hidden under a charming façade, having lurked there. She shivered, but not from cold.

Positioning herself for a first run, Melissa pushed off. Her depression began to lift: the act of skiing had an exhilarating effect on body and mind. The new, long skis were as fast as the ski shop owner had guaranteed they would be; she became engrossed in the absorbing challenge of mastering them and of becoming comfortable with the new, almost knee-high, boots.

Time slipped by unnoticed. A very accomplished skier, she made numerous practice runs before consciously realizing that each time she reached the bottom there was a young man, the same young man, standing there observing her. Studiously ignoring him, she decided she was ready to go on to a higher, more demanding course.

The slopes were fairly well populated, and the line at the next-higher lift was not more than six or eight people deep. Somewhat uncomfortable when the stranger who had been watching her moved along beside her in the line and they were paired together on the chair, Melissa chalked it up to mere coincidence. As they steadily rose through the clearing above the trees in the still silence of the winter day, she didn't so much as glance at him, having no desire to strike up even a casual conversation with anyone. Her weary mind was preoccupied, though her well-tuned body was seeking a challenge.

Melissa pushed off from the little slope that went from the lift to her first steep run of the day. Reveling in the freedom of maneuvering through the white powdery snow that sprayed out like a filmy white fan around her, she snaked down the long run. Perhaps if I ski fast enough, I can outrun my worries and my heartaches, she thought with fleeting hopefulness, but Brandon's heart-wrenchingly handsome face appeared in her traitorous mind. No, I guess that's not possible, she conceded. I can never outrun thoughts of him.

Dimly, she became conscious of another skier who, surprisingly, was matching her own speed. At the bottom of the run as she made her way back to the lift, she realized it was the same young man who had been watching her and then had ridden beside her.

When the same seating arrangement repeated itself on their next lift ride, she ventured a glance at him. It seemed strange to have the same partner on consecutive rides, but undoubtedly it had happened before on other days with other people and she just hadn't noticed it. Goggles obscured his eyes, although no snow was falling, and the chin of his long face was nestled in a dark turtleneck sweater. With a knit hat pulled down tightly over forehead and ears, little of his face was exposed.

The third time he was her partner on the chair she became annoyed. It was definitely not coincidental, as she had hoped. After this run down she would go back into the day lodge for a warm drink and, more importantly, to rid herself of his unsolicited company.

Much to her consternation, he followed her off the slopes into the lodge. Quickly ordering a cup of coffee, she carried it to one of the long bare common tables at the far side of the cavernous room. After the stranger had purchased his coffee, he clomped across the room to the table where she was seated. Goggles pushed back over his hatband revealed pale, almost colorless, blue eyes. Smiling ingratiatingly, he sat down opposite her.

"Hope you don't mind," he said pleasantly.

"I *do* mind," Melissa replied, looking him coldly in the face, hoping this rebuke would cause him to leave her alone.

Unaffected, ignoring her rebuff, he remarked, "I notice you're alone and I'm alone. I thought we could get acquainted." The fawning smile was meant to be charming.

Fleetingly she wondered if he might be a lonely serviceman from one of the nearby military bases; however, looking closely, it suddenly struck her how his sharp features and general appearance resembled those of Jason Leonard. Could they all be wrong? Could this be . . . ? Her mind refused to finish the question. No, she chided herself, you're keyed up enough to imagine a killer behind every tree. But she didn't like the way he was looking at her, although she couldn't tell why. . . . It was almost possessive, she realized with a start, placing her hands around the steaming cup to warm chilled fingers.

"You're a good skier," he said. "I've been watching you."

"I know you have," she answered sharply, deep blue eyes cold as the icicles that hung daggerlike from the eaves of the lodge roof, "and I don't like it!" Her fingers nervously searched for the cup handle.

Undaunted, he continued to grin. "You're hard to approach, aren't you?" The comment met her stony countenance. "That's good, that's good." His head nodded in approval. "But seriously," the expression on his thin face changed to concern, "I don't think you should be skiing alone."

"Why not?" she asked, raising the cup to her lips. Interested to hear his answer, she suddenly realized she'd been suspicious of him all along, even from the moment she'd first noticed he was watching her. The cup rattled as she placed it back on the saucer.

"Because they might not have the right man in jail," he replied calmly, blowing the steam away before taking a sip of his coffee.

"You don't think they do?" Melissa asked, momentarily startled that his words so closely echoed her own thoughts. "What makes you say that?"

A warning flashed into her mind. At once she remembered that many heinous criminals are caught because they're compelled to tell someone about their dark deeds—their twisted, warped minds can't tolerate someone else having the fame and notoriety for what they've done. A compulsive, uncontrollable need to tell someone that they are responsible, that they deserve the credit, often flushes them into the open. Her heart missed a beat. Would he dare brag to her about . . .

"All the police did was go up on a mountain, ask a few questions, then arrest and jail the first man they saw who happened to have long blond hair. From what I've heard they don't have an awful lot of evidence, outside of some terrified girl's identification," he answered easily.

Melissa couldn't see his hair because of the way his hat was pulled down—it could be any length. She experienced a moment of quiet panic as she searched her mind for what to do. If she continued talking with him, he might turn out to be some innocent guy who'd end up with the mistaken notion that she'd led him on, that she was interested in him. If she stopped talking with him, he might go on to some other girl—and if there was the slightest possibility he was the man the whole community feared, she would lose her chance to prove it. But how could she prove it? Facts, Brandon had said. But what facts . . . short of getting herself killed?

"I don't want to talk about it." She shuddered involuntarily. Her imagination was carrying her away. Jason Leonard was the killer—Brandon was sure.

Seemingly pleased with her reaction, a grin spread over the man's face. "Don't worry, I'll take care of you," he said familiarly, with an absurd implication of intimacy. "First, I'll get us another cup of coffee."

Her self-proclaimed protector swung his legs over the bench and rose from the table, taking her cup with his. Scrutinizing his tall, slightly stoop-shouldered form, Melissa tried to memorize every detail of his clothing as he walked away, but to her dismay it was just ordinary dark blue skiwear with no distinguishing features. She couldn't even detect the brand. He could be any one of a dozen people she had seen during the day.

She didn't want another cup of coffee, but she stayed seated where she was, knowing she was safe in the lodge. But safe from what? He really hadn't done anything suspicious. Undoubtedly, in her keyed-up state, she was letting her imagination run wild. Accustomed to brushing off unwanted advances from unattached men, she silently admitted it wasn't strange for a man to be concerned about her safety during a time like this. But what if he asked her to ski with him again? Should she risk it? She was confident she could outrun him on the hill if he tried anything there; still . . .

If only she could ask someone who he was! Looking carefully around the almost empty room, she found it contained no acquaintances: most people were out on the slopes. How she wished someone would speak to him so she would know whether he had friends around. But he purchased the coffee without acknowledging anyone and returned to the table, managing not to spill any of the hot liquid from either cup in spite of the clumsiness of his ski boots on the bare floor.

"Here you are, Melissa." He set her cup on the table.

"How do you know my name?" she asked in outright hostility. She couldn't bear to think of touching the cup he had brought her.

"From your skis," he replied smoothly.

It was true that her name was engraved on the tips, she realized. She'd had it done for purposes of identification, but maybe it hadn't been such a good idea. Perhaps it added to his unwarranted sense of familiarity.

"Do you live around here?" she asked, her fingernails nervously tapping on the heavily varnished surface of the table.

"I have a little place nearby," he answered vaguely, an amused look in his eyes. Skin crawling, Melissa had the uneasy feeling he was a cat toying with a mouse.

"Are you employed here?" she asked again, hoping for more information. He had evaded her first question very effectively and, she knew, quite deliberately.

"Yes, you might say that." He grinned again, obviously

enjoying not answering her questions fully—playing the game to the hilt.

Well, he could play without her. Decidedly disturbed, as well as physically uncomfortable, she rose to leave. The coffee had made her too warm and her cheeks were beginning to flush from a combination of nerves and heat. She didn't want to be near this man any longer, even if he wasn't the fiend she half imagined him to be.

Beginning to doubt her ability to judge any situation rationally, she questioned her own perceptions. Perhaps Brandon was right: perhaps women were too emotional. I'll get my imagination under control, she vowed determinedly. I must be more overwrought than I realized.

"Thank you for the coffee," she said curtly and left the table, leaving the cup conspicuously untouched.

Once past the incoming stream of skiers who were now beginning to pack the steps as they stamped the snow from their boots before entering the lodge, Melissa breathed deeply. Soft puffy flakes of snow had begun to fall, and though it was only early afternoon, the darkness of the arctic night was closing in. Soon, she knew, powerful lights would illuminate selected runs for night skiing.

The area outside the lodge was filled with red-cheeked skiers; those who'd decided to call it a day and were busily collecting and packing up their gear to head home, and those of a heartier breed who were taking a breather to meet friends in the lodge and discuss plans for the evening over a hot toddy. Amidst them Melissa stepped into her skis, picked up her poles, and started for the lift. She wanted to look behind her to see if she were being followed but resisted the impulse. Jumping on the first available chair, she sighed with relief to see she had no other seat occupant.

When she got off, her eyes were drawn toward the other chairs climbing inexorably up the mountainside. There he was, only five chairs back! She quickly pushed off and skied to another lift that would take her still higher up the cloud-shrouded mountain. The snow fell harder, filling the encroaching darkness with its silent whiteness.

There was no wait at all this time. She got on and looking back over her shoulder saw him skiing toward the lift she was being carried on. He *was* following her! There was no doubt about it now.

All naïve ill-conceived thoughts of gathering facts were swept from her mind, replaced by a new fear. Even if Jason were the original murderer, others might appear. Often in sensation cases, copycat killers emerged. *Dear God, could he be one of those?* Either way, she had to get down the mountain as quickly as possible and stay inside the lodge until Brandon and Jana returned.

Dropping off the chair, she began the long difficult descent down the fresh light blanket of snow. She couldn't even see the lodge below from this height. Her knees trembled, and in her fright she almost fell several times, excellent skier though she was. She could hear him calling behind her.

"Melissa . . . wait! I'm not going to hurt you!" The hissing voice carried on the wind.

Heart pounding violently from exertion and fear, she stem-turned through an unexpected patch of moguls. Unable to catch herself, she lost her balance and fell. Her ski released its binding, and she slid down the icy incline to where it had braked. Hat and goggles had been knocked off, but she lost no precious time looking for them. *Time!* her mind screamed. *Time! . . . Did she have only moments of life left?* Her sole aim and only hope was to snap her boot into its binding.

He was approaching! The sound of his skis on the moguls caused her almost to faint from fear. The tall, dark figure loomed through the crystalline curtain just as she finally managed to get to her feet. Closing in, he was at last beside her, his grasping fingers reaching out for her—she felt them brush her jacket. Her heart threatened to burst within her breast, so violent was its pounding. Fear constricted her throat. She pulled away an instant before he could take hold and swept breathlessly down—down—down—through the swirling, frigid, suffocating storm.

Dimly she made out the lights of the lodge. Praying fervently for courage not to falter in the last few frantic moments of flight, she knew she should slow down to avoid colliding with other skiers who might be shielded from her view by the thick white fall, but she couldn't do it. That danger seemed nothing in comparison to the threat closing in on her, ready to overtake her if she made the slightest stumble or error in judgment. The horrible knowledge that her pursuer was close behind—hissing out her name—*that he had touched her!*—increased her panic.

At last, strength and hope almost gone, she reached the haven of the steamy-windowed lodge. Recklessly kicking off her skis before coming to a full stop, she half stumbled, half ran, as if in the throes of a hideous nightmare—heedless of everything except her need to get inside. She pulled open the heavy door, and warm air blasted against her snow-burned face. A frenzied scream tore at her throat, but she was too winded and spent to utter a sound.

Oblivious to the curious stares of people sprawled comfortably around the blazing fire, she sank back against the door, secure in the knowledge that she had eluded the grasping tentacles of her assailant. She was safe! He wouldn't dare follow her inside! Snow covered her like a mantle—her hair and even her eyelashes were laden with the sticky wet whiteness. Overwhelmed with a pervasive heavy weakness, trembling violently from physical exhaustion and emotional relief, her slight body began to sink to the floor. Strong arms stopped her fall, sweeping her fragile snow-covered form up against the comfort of a solid masculine chest in loving protection.

"What's the matter, Snowbird!" Brandon Kade's deep voice demanded urgently. "What happened?"

Weak arms reached up to cling to the steel of his neck. His

familiar strength consoled her, but she continued to shake in paroxysms of remembered fear.

Before she could answer, the door opened. Incredibly, Melissa saw the man who had pursued her mercilessly through the blinding storm walk into the lodge. In dazed shock she watched him nonchalantly stomp the snow from his boots, pull off his gloves, and reach up to remove his snow-encrusted hat. Could she be hallucinating? He calmly stood there as though nothing out of the ordinary had occurred. Gradually the reality of what she was seeing registered; raising his fogged goggles, he grinned at the sight of her.

"That's him!" she gasped, barely able to choke out the words. "He's been chasing me! *Chasing me!*" Her voice ended in a sob, as she buried her face in the warmth of Brandon's broad chest.

Carefully lowering Melissa to her feet, while still keeping her within the protective circle of his arm, Brandon's body stiffened with silent, barely controlled rage. Quietly, in razor-sharp tones, he confronted the man Melissa had accused. "Who the hell are you? And just what do you think you're doing?"

The grin disappeared from the face of the stranger, driven away by the steely anger in the eyes of the powerful man before him.

"Just hold on a minute. I've got I.D." The blond man hurriedly unzipped his jacket, reached into an inside pocket, and produced a leather folder.

Brandon snatched it from his hand and closely examined the documents it contained.

"So you're a private cop. You still haven't answered my question. What were you doing chasing Mrs. Bennett down the mountain?" Brandon pressed.

"I wasn't chasing her, I was trying to keep her in sight—to protect her," he offered defensively. "That's what I've been trying to do all day. And it hasn't been easy, I can tell you that." Indignant, he retrieved his identification and carefully tucked it away.

"*Protect me?*" Melissa asked incredulously. "Who made you my protector?" she parried, anger flaring anew, overcoming the debilitating exhaustion of terror.

"Mr. Bennett, your father-in-law," he shot back almost insolently. "He hired our agency right after Christmas. We've been on your tail ever since. I was sent today because I'm the best skier we've got."

Every detail of his story rang true. This accounted for Laurence's relaxed attitude and for the unaccountable familiarity with which this man had treated her earlier. It had all been just a ghastly mistake. A feeling of sick relief rose inside her as Melissa hid her face in Brandon's sweater, too humiliated to look at the man again.

"I apologize if I've frightened her," the man said, insolence changing to uneasiness.

"I should report you for your unprofessional handling of the situation," Brandon charged.

The young man's characteristic brashness asserted itself at this reprimand. "I think my actions were totally justified. The snowfall was heavy today and I needed to be as close to her as possible. She's headstrong and foolhardy. She needs to be protected."

"Consider yourself dismissed," Brandon said curtly at this display of rudeness and ineptitude. "I know I can speak for Mr. Bennett in this matter." He waved the fellow off with frosty disdain.

Melissa's fright, though unfounded, had been terrifyingly real, physically and emotionally draining—her body still trembled as Brandon led her to the table where Jana sat finishing her snack.

"Come on, let's get out of here," Brandon said to the child. Her round eyes full of questions, she obediently helped him gather up their things.

"What happened to Mommy?"

"She just stayed out too long, and she's cold," Brandon answered smoothly. "Let's take her home now."

"Are you really all right, Mommy?"

"Yes, honey." Melissa mustered what she hoped was a convincing grin.

Melissa was grateful for the support of Brandon's strong arm as he led her and Jana out of the lodge. They found her hastily abandoned skis on the rack, placed there by a passing ski patrol. Brandon stopped to scoop them up before they walked through the no longer menacing, silently falling snow to the parking lot.

After Jana had fallen asleep on the backseat, happily exhausted from her day on the trails, Melissa, choking with sobs of relief, recounted her horrid adventure.

Sympathetic, Brandon took her hand in his. "It's over now, Snowbird. Believe me, I understand. What you went through was as devastating as it would have been had he been the real killer. That's the power suspicion has. It makes enemies of the most well-meaning people." He slid his arm around her shoulders. "Lean over this way. Let me hold you while you lie back and relax."

They drove the rest of the way in silence, but Melissa found the silence comforting. Her head lay against the solid throbbing of his heart—she needed the security of his touch. Unwillingly her mind returned to the slopes as she relived the terror of her escape. Waves of compassion for the innocent victims who had met their hideous fate in the cold snow arose in her. Unlike her, they'd never returned from their last run. At her convulsive shudder, Brandon pulled her closer, seeming to understand without words, placing his cheek against her damp hair.

Melissa sensed there was more behind his actions than simple concern—a deep, underlying well of intimacy lay between them, undisturbed and unsullied by the surface storms that had beset them, that had at times torn them apart. A common well which, she began to suspect as his hand sensuously kneaded her arm, they both wanted to drink from deeply and fully. She knew memories of this day would haunt her sleep for many years to come—she also knew she could never have gotten through it without Brandon.

At the condominium Jana awakened, groggily rubbing her eyes at the familiar sound of the garage door lifting in response to the signal from the automatic opener. Melissa helped her from the car into the condo through the kitchen door while Brandon unloaded the ski rack and placed the gear at the side of the garage.

Melissa looked up from her kneeling position on the floor where she was helping Jana from her ski clothes to see Brandon's large figure filling the frame of her kitchen door.

"I need to use your car for a while. Will you be all right while I'm gone?" he asked solicitously. "I'll be back around nine. Melissa, will you have dinner with me tonight at my hotel? Get someone to spend the night with Jana." His words, rounded with meaning, assumed her acceptance, yet his intent gaze prolonged the moment as if fearing a refusal.

She rose to her feet with a smile. Somehow she wanted to believe the moment was full of promise. She had to have this evening with him. But how? Ordinarily without question Jana could have stayed with Dad and Irene, but Melissa knew they would be out enjoying the last full night of festivities. Dad will still be gambling at dawn, she thought, wracking her brain for a solution. Her housekeeper, Betty! She'd been complaining just the other day that she didn't have dates for any of the big events.

"I'll ask my housekeeper to stay," Melissa called in answer as Brandon strode out the door toward the car, an enigma as usual. She stood in wonder leaning against the doorjamb as he drove out of sight; then she pressed the automatic button to lower the garage door. I'll never understand him, she thought in bewilderment.

CHAPTER FIFTEEN

Fortunately Betty had been home when Melissa had called and had come right over. She'd fixed dinner for Jana and herself, and they were now contentedly occupied playing a quiet board game. At least that problem had been solved easily enough.

In her room laying out the things she planned to wear for the evening, Melissa wondered what could possibly happen next in her life. Her horrid fright of the afternoon had dissipated at Brandon's touch—that tall, maddeningly magnetic man seemed to hold the power to hurt or heal her at will. He'd come immediately when she'd asked for his help and had held her protectively in his powerful arms when she had needed him so desperately.

How could she have been so foolish? she asked herself, reaching up to the top closet shelf to take down a pair of black pumps. Had she not chosen to reject him when he'd offered his love, she could have had the luxury of being held in his arms forever. What could I have thought was important enough to have stood between us? she wondered as she searched a drawer for her black lingerie. My career? My independence? Imagined problems with Irene and Laurence dissolved with no help from me—wouldn't my fears concerning my career have done the same? She paused, holding her black slip to her breast. No. Deep within herself she knew her longing for professional fulfillment would have surfaced in time if she had chosen to cast it to the wind in her obsessive need for Brandon. But still . . . were professional accomplishments of any real importance if she couldn't share them with her love? And Brandon *is* my love, my *only* love.

Bathing, lavishly soaping her tired legs with a sweetly scented bar, she was acutely conscious of the slender body he had touched so intimately during the magic days they'd spent together in the past. Her skin colored with a warm rosy hue at the memory. A faint glimmer of hope struggled in her breast while optimism warred with pessimism. Pessimism won out.

What had really changed? They'd reached some sort of friendly truce, she knew. Perhaps from the wreckage of their love they could at least be friends. Perhaps that was what his trip was all about. Perhaps he, too, needed to resolve their relationship to a friendly level free of bitterness and rancor. A tear slid down her cheek as she thought how much more it could have been. Only if things had been different, a small voice of reason nagged within her brain.

Stepping from the tub, she wrapped herself in a large absorbent towel. The dinner dress she'd selected was black velvet; cut deeply to the cleft of her full breasts, it would cling seductively to the curves of her hips and thighs. She'd bought it in San Francisco on an impulse, and afterwards had wondered why. Looking down at it, she thought about the dinner Brandon had planned and what the evening held in store. Doubts piled themselves one on top of the other, filling her mind.

Sitting on the satin-covered bench at the end of the bed, she pulled on her gossamer panty hose, thinking back over the events of the afternoon. His taking me in his arms was a natural human reaction—any man would have done that, she told herself. His other actions were probably just a continuation of his effort to comfort me, nothing more.

He'd left with no explanation as to where he was going. Though, she admitted, he had every reason to assume she would know he was going to work on the case. In fact, he may just want to ask me more about the case over dinner. She shuddered. I was surely in no condition to be helpful this afternoon.

Her thoughts continued to taunt and mock her for her false sense of hopefulness as she artfully applied the little makeup she used to enhance her natural beauty. Her taut body ached yearningly for the release only he could give. They would make love tonight—she was sure he wanted it as much as she. But where would she be left after that?

She'd made a fool of herself once when she had begged for his love—she wouldn't put herself in that degrading position again. Most likely she should be thankful her pleas had been met with rejection. Her overwhelming love for him had caused her to seek a union which could have resulted only in disillusionment and pain for both of them.

As much as I love him, almost more than life itself, I couldn't live with the repudiation of my principles year in and year out. I could never have lived the life of "wifey" to the "great man." We would have ended up another dry statistic: divorced due to irreconcilable differences. No, marriage was for life, she believed; she could never have borne that.

She fastened diamond studs in her ears, then hesitated before reaching to the back of her jewelry drawer for an oblong box. Slowly she lifted the lid, revealing the golden medallion Brandon had given her that long-ago day in Mexico . . . the day she had first given herself to him in love. She held it across the palm of her hand before carefully fastening its chain around her neck. Let him think what he would.

Looking at her reflection in the mirror after she stepped into the sophisticated gown, she was surprised. The wide-set eyes that looked back at her were those of a woman . . . a woman who had lived the incredible heights of passion and the lonely desolation of pain and longing. Having grown and matured through this experience, painful though it had been, she knew only too well her love for Brandon Kade was not fleeting infatuation, but rather the full-blown love of a grown woman for an accomplished commanding man.

How she wished that Brandon could have accepted her as she was with her wants and needs and desires—or that she could have been the woman he had wanted her to be. She'd gambled with love, desiring to be the mistress of her own fate, and had lost. But no matter the outcome, she could look ahead, knowing her life was infinitely richer for having had the experiences and memories he had given her.

Hearing the crunch of tires on the snow-covered drive promptly at nine, Melissa nervously slipped into her white fox coat and met Brandon at the door. In the soft glow of the outside lights she stopped, caught by his intimate gaze. It seemed to her at this moment they shared the same mind, the same spirit. For a long interval neither spoke or moved, fearful of breaking the magic spell that bound them. Each beheld the perfection of the other—as if sensing the wholeness and rightness of their being together. Cut off from the world and reminders of their erratic past by the purity of the falling flakes, they moved together, walking as though enchanted to the waiting car, his hand lightly holding her arm.

As he drove through the crowded streets, Brandon debated with himself. How should he approach the woman who sat so calmly by his side? What were her thoughts and feelings? He was almost glad that idiot on the mountain had driven her into his arms. But how to get her there again, where she belonged forever . . . how would he accomplish that?

And what about Jeffreys? The young D.A. was an up-and-comer; he'd known that immediately upon meeting him. Discreet inquiries had revealed that Jeffreys had strong political backing, including that of Laurence Bennett, and a promising future.

He'd also learned that some people believed the D.A. was more than mildly interested in the young Mrs. Bennett. Was that only gossip? he wondered. Melissa had certainly seemed evasive when Jeffreys's name had come up in their very first conversation; she'd seemed uncomfortable even discussing him. Well, there was no use sitting here tormenting himself with unanswered questions. He'd have to take the initiative and plunge right in.

His gruff words broke the silent spell. "I met your friend Jeffreys today. Nice guy."

"Yes, he is." Her reply seemed cautious. Did she understand that he was obliquely inquiring about her relationship with Darryl?

"Did you mention me to him?" she asked. The windshield wipers continued their hypnotic course, sweeping the oncoming snow back and forth in a semicircle. Was he imagining it or was she unduly anxious?

"You asked me not to," he answered. Was it as he feared? Was there more between her and Jeffreys than a business relationship? Could he wrest her away from the arms of an Alaskan, considering her love of family and home?

"I'm glad you didn't," she remarked quickly, offering nothing more.

"Why is that?" he asked, convinced now that he did indeed have a serious rival for her affections.

"Because I haven't had a chance to explain to him why I called you. I want to be the one to tell him that I asked you to look into defending Jason Leonard. If you'd taken the case you'd have been courtroom rivals. As a friend I should have prepared Darryl for that possibility. I'm still worried about how you explained your presence in Anchorage and your interest in the case."

Brandon let out a sigh of relief at this disclosure. "Believe me, you don't have anything to worry about there."

She smiled, visibly relaxing against the back of her seat.

Was that all there was to it? Brandon wondered, feeling his spirits buoy.

Still he couldn't let it rest there. "Are you sure that's all you were worried about?"

Innocent sapphire eyes directly confronted his. "Yes, of course. What else could there be?"

He groaned inwardly. Lord how he loved this woman! Confidently he wheeled under the cover of the hotel portico. Handing the keys to the waiting attendant, he helped Melissa from the low-slung car.

She could feel a slight tremor in the hand that enclosed her elbow and heard a sharp intake of breath as she emerged to stand facing him.

"You're lovely tonight, Melissa," he murmured. His eyes hungrily clung to hers.

As she stepped through the glass doors into the lobby, a pandemonium of high-spirited voices broke raucously upon their ears, shattering the magic, intimate cocoon that had softly enveloped them from the moment she'd stepped from the condo. Melissa sank back against Brandon, momentarily recoiling from the assault to her senses, unwilling somehow to join the world and face its problems again.

Well-dressed people, in boisterous bunches, were waiting in front of the bank of elevators at the far side of the lobby to be taken to the luxurious dining room and bar on the top floor. Brandon's hand on her elbow deliberately guided her progress through the crowd directly toward them.

"Melissa!" The familiar voice of Darryl Jeffreys called her name.

She turned to see him emerging from a group of friends. The wide smile on his face reflected his pleasure at seeing her; her stomach churned guiltily at the sight. At the same time she felt Brandon's hand close possessively on her elbow pulling her closer to his side.

"Kade," Darryl said, nodding in greeting to Brandon, a surprised look in his eyes.

"Jeffreys," Brandon responded, his voice curt.

Melissa watched comprehension register on Darryl's face as he looked from her to Brandon and then back to her again. Until this moment, she knew, Darryl hadn't guessed how well she and Brandon knew one another. The possessiveness with which Brandon held her arm and the surprisingly challenging look in his eyes bespoke more between them than a casual relationship. Having come to know Darryl well, she realized his astute mind was grasping the implications of several things that she hadn't been able to explain to him: her cool reception of his romantic advances, her reluctance to discuss the sensational criminal case Brandon had been conducting last fall, and Brandon's sudden appearance in Anchorage coupled with his interest in the ski slope murderer. Melissa saw it all become clear to Darryl Jeffreys in an instant. She knew she should have been more open with him, but really what had there been to tell?

Was that a flicker of hurt in his eyes? Lord, she hoped not. Having suffered so much herself at love's hands, she had no desire to inflict even a moment of pain on him. She knew every available young woman in Alaska would jump at the chance to have Darryl at her side. If he was hurt at seeing where her true feelings lay, it had been inevitable. They'd both known since before Christmas, although he hadn't been willing to admit it, that they could never share more than friendship. She felt sure that though he cared for her in his own way, his was not a passion so overwhelming in its intensity that he couldn't replace her in his affections.

"Care to join us upstairs?" Darryl asked after just a moment's hesitation, his friendly invitation encompassing them both.

Melissa smiled, truly appreciating his urbane generosity. This display of well-mannered friendliness seemed an expression of understanding of her love for Brandon.

"Maybe later," Brandon countered, smoothly if unconvincingly.

They entered the elevator with Darryl's party of talking, laughing friends, several of whom Melissa knew. As the elevator ascended she introduced Brandon all around. She could barely conceal amusement at some of their reactions—mawkish stares or gushing responses to his charming acknowledgments—and she couldn't help remembering her timidity at the thought of meeting him for the first time.

Automatically she started forward when the elevator reached the restaurant, but Brandon held her back as the others surged into the mezzanine. Darryl turned as he stepped from the elevator, his eyes quizzically seeking hers. Catching on quickly, he knowingly winked at her, a devilish look on his face. Melissa blushed crimson. Mercifully the doors shut out the others' inquisitive eyes.

Descending two floors in peaceful spacious silence in stark contrast to the crowded noisy atmosphere that had prevailed only seconds before, heart pounding so nervously its throbbing seemed to fill the void, Melissa consciously decided to stop operating on the basis of assumption where Brandon was concerned. It's time for me to stop resisting and to let down my defenses. I've damned him without a trial. I've set the parameters of our relationship. I was the one who insisted on a strictly business arrangement. I've never given him a chance.

Feeling the velvet of her dress touch her breasts, she glanced at the whiteness of his tucked shirtfront exposed from under his dark cashmere overcoat. The lady in black velvet and the gentleman in a dinner jacket? Dressed for business? *Who were they trying to kid?* She had been so determined not to expose her vulnerability to Brandon again that she had been actively building walls of resistance between them.

Melissa looked up at him, her lips curving into a sweet smile. . . . I want this night, am willing to settle for only this one last night with him if that's the way it has to be. In reply, he merely smiled into the deep blue pools that were her eyes as they walked hand in hand down the hushed quiet of the hallway. Melissa waited quietly, unembarrassed, while Brandon unlocked the door to what was obviously his suite.

In a glance Melissa took in the table for two that had been set in front of the large floor-to-ceiling window that looked out over the twinkling lights of the city through the softly falling snow. The rich white linen of the tablecloth and napkins, the fine platinum-rimmed bone china, the clear crystal goblets, and the heavy silver flatware gleamed in the softly muted light that suffused the room. The faintly spicy aroma of velvety red winter roses, mingled with pine, permeated the air.

Brandon helped her remove her elegant full-length coat, his eyes traveling over her body. An expressive eyebrow raised almost imperceptibly at the glitter of the gold pendant resting between the swell of her breasts. He looked at her, a question in his eyes. For a trusting instant she let him glimpse the hidden secrets of her heart before quickly averting her gaze. Her body trembled, electrified by the response his bold eyes sparked within her.

"I thought we'd have dinner up here where we could talk. It would be impossible in the dining room," he explained, gesturing toward the elaborately set table. "Besides, *I* wanted to order tonight," he teased.

"Not escargots, I hope," she said with a grin.

"Not unless you particularly want them," he replied with a straight face, his eyes twinkling. "Never could stand the things myself." They laughed at their shared memory.

Relaxed, Melissa sank down on the couch facing the large picture window. Her eyes followed his every movement. He looked younger tonight, more himself—vital, as she'd remembered him.

He removed the loosened cork from a bottle in the wine cooler and poured them each a goblet of translucent ruby red Cabernet Sauvignon. Skin glowing like polished ivory in the dim light set off by the sheen of her velvet gown, Melissa accepted her glass before he settled himself beside her.

"So," he began, looking at her with the full attention of his dynamic presence, causing a weakness to spread through her body, "you had a real fright today." She nodded, shuddering at the memory.

"It was truly awful. I've never been so scared in my life. I can't stop thinking of those poor girls for whom it didn't end so fortunately." She added to herself: in your arms, remembering the immediate sense of relief she'd experienced when he'd appeared at her side offering solace and protection. "I'm afraid it's going to be a long time before I can go skiing again." She sighed deeply.

Abruptly he stood and walked over to the window. His perfectly proportioned physique seemed larger than life. Looking over the city toward the snow-covered heights that rose ridge upon ridge toward the sky, he said meaningfully, "Those slopes are safe. I would never have let you go up there alone if I hadn't been sure of that."

"You're absolutely sure that Jason Leonard is—is the . . ." She couldn't bring herself to finish the sentence. Her eyes clouded sorrowfully.

"Yes," he turned toward her, a solemn look on his face. "I'm afraid so."

"How can you be so sure?" she asked in a strained voice, placing her glass on the low table before her. "You've been here such a short time."

"Snowbird, I haven't been completely honest with you. I started working on this case the minute the news of the first incident was reported, knowing how you like to ski. Actually I considered hiring a security guard for you myself, but from what you'd told me of him, I was confident your dad had already taken care of that."

Stunned by this revelation, Melissa sat in shocked silence.

He continued. "Similar murders occurred in New Zealand last summer, which is their winter, you know. The description of the suspect in those cases was almost identical to the one compiled here. Yesterday, when I questioned Leonard about his whereabouts during the past year, it all came together—he didn't even deny being there when the murders occurred. I immediately had the evidence the New Zealand police had collected sent by satellite to Seattle and then flown up to Jeffreys's office. He called me early this morning, before you picked me up, to tell me the results. The fingerprints they had are virtually conclusive evidence in themselves. Of course, there's more groundwork to be done, but Jeffreys seems quite competent. He should be able to get an easy conviction."

At the mention of Darryl's name Melissa's mind was sent reeling as wave after wave of shame swept over her. Her face reddened. All the self-confidence she had so painstakingly tried to instill in herself over the past few years was gone.

"I feel"—she began searching for a word to express the contempt she felt for herself—"stupid . . . absolutely stupid." But that wasn't strong enough to convey the self-recrimination with which she was scourging herself. "No. Asinine is a better word. I really believed in the innocence of that man. How could I have been so . . . *so . . . utterly—stupid!*" she finished lamely, biting her lip to stave off tears.

"Don't feel that way, darling," Brandon said softly. "He comes on as a most charming person. Since his arrest, he's convinced many people of his innocence. His personality is strong, but twisted. I believe the court psychiatrists will find he's a sociopath, not a psychopath, which makes it all the more difficult to understand him. Remember how I made you promise to stay away from him the night you called me?" She nodded mutely. "I had a hunch even then he was the man."

His face took on the tender loving look of possessiveness it had held that wonderful first night on the beach—the look she had never dreamed she would actually see again.

His voice grew husky with emotion. "Imagine how I felt

when you burst wildly in that door looking like the very devil was after you. I thought I'd made the mistake of my life." As he passed his hand across his forehead, hesitating, Melissa thought vaguely how very strange it was to see Brandon actually unsure of himself. "I nearly knocked over the table jumping up to get to you."

He closed the distance between them. Allowing herself to be pulled up into his arms, she hid her face in the soft cloth of his jacket.

"I've been stupid about so many things, I don't think I can ever forgive myself," she lamented. "I've made a mess of my job with my father-in-law, I've interfered in Darryl's work and really made a mess there too. To put it bluntly, I've screwed up everything I've touched—even us." She whispered the last, lost hope causing her voice to quaver.

"Just growing pains," he murmured against the softness of her golden hair. His arm encircling her waist was strong and firm, pressing her against the warmth of his body. "Don't worry about it. We learn from mistakes. God knows" —his voice caught raggedly—"I've learned from mine. But you've been right all along about the most important things." His lips found her smooth temple, their titillating caresses causing her pulse to race wildly.

Drawing a tremulous breath, she waited expectantly for him to go on. Gently, with one strong hand, he lifted her face from where she'd nestled it against his chest, looking deeply into the depths of her eyes. She reeled dizzily under the impact of his gaze.

"Darling," he drawled huskily, "look at me." Reluctantly she complied, finding an expression on his face that she'd never seen before—that she couldn't define. "You were right about me—I wasn't the man for you to marry," his tantalizing lips whispered.

Her one secret dream, the one she had managed to conceal even from herself since the moment she had placed the call to ask him to come, the dream that somehow they would overcome all obstacles to be reconciled in love, was shattered in an instant. Her heart turned to ice; staggering alarm contorted her lovely features. She pulled back, trying to lower her head from the brutal impact of his words, but his strong hand held her chin firmly.

"But maybe with a lifetime of help, I can learn to be."

His eyes clouded mistily, then his mouth closed over hers in devastatingly sweet domination, claiming her lips as he never had before. In an instant Melissa felt as if she were riding a wave of pure emotion that was transporting her from the cold, bottomless depths of despair to the ultimate fiery heights of pure unreasoning euphoria. Dreaming or waking, it mattered not; surging on the crest of sweet rapture, she abandoned herself to the oblivion of desire, until, uncomprehendingly, she felt his lips pull away from the consuming embrace.

Her searching eyes sought his sun-dark face for explanation, while he gripped her in the circle of his arms holding the length of her body to his.

"A man—a person"—her clearing mind noticed this uncharacteristic concession—"doesn't like being told he's wrong . . . doesn't like not being accepted the way he is. I'd built my career on learning not to feel compassion for my clients—or, I realize now, for anyone else. I had fallen into the habit of testing or mistrusting any random hint of happiness that might come my way.

"And you"—he looked down at her, his quicksilver eyes pleading for understanding—"you held too much power over me. I couldn't accept it; I couldn't allow myself to succumb to your needs or demands. I couldn't lose control of my life to one small woman. Somehow, crazy as it seems now, loving you so much confused me—in some irrational way it made me feel less of a man. Can you understand that at all?"

"Yes," she murmured.

"Melissa." He spoke only her name, but that was enough,

as they clung tightly to one another in the beginnings of true understanding.

"I looked at myself long and hard after our encounter on the boat and didn't like what I saw, but I wasn't prepared to change. I realized it wasn't you but myself that I didn't trust. I didn't like knowing I was so weak where you were concerned." His voice was almost a rasp of emotion-roughened tension.

"Remember how I told you I would take you everywhere with me?"

She nodded. How *well* she remembered.

"For the longest time that statement stuck in my head as the best I had to offer you, until gradually the meaning of what I had said sunk into my thick skull. It's true—I was just going to make you an appendage to my 'glorious career,' as you pointed out. You were right to refuse me on those grounds."

She opened her lips to speak, but he stilled them with the soft touch of his.

"Wait. . . . I'm not finished. I want you to hear it all. After you left San Francisco I was still damned angry with you, but the murders up here caused me to worry for your safety. That's when I really began to see the light. I realized my career, which I'd prized above all else, was nothing . . . an empty shell that I'd spent my life creating. Building it had taken everything human out of me. You helped me get back in touch with my feelings, and it was painful. My life became a black, meaningless void without you. I didn't realize my damnable pride could cause me to suffer such agony." He shook his head in disbelief.

"It wasn't just women for whom I had no respect, as you and Julia seemed to feel so acutely—I realized I'd lost my respect for everyone. What an egotistical jerk I was! I'd become used to getting my own way in the courtroom, and as my reputation grew, I was able to have almost everything in my life the way I wanted it, when I wanted it.

"Then you came along." He groaned. Her face hidden, Melissa couldn't help but smile, as she tightened her arms around his slim waist. "I guess I thought just because I wanted you, it was preordained I would have you. I've acted like a spoiled brat in a toy shop who can't have everything he sees," he admitted contritely.

"In La Jolla I thought everything was going great for us. That night on the beach was absolute perfection—more than I deserved from you." His eyes softened with the memory.

"You see, I had to have you from the moment I first laid eyes on you. To my egotistical mind, it was as if you had been created and put there only for me. When I told you that you belonged to me, I really thought that was how it was to be: you would be mine because I wanted you, not because you wanted me. Now I can't believe that I didn't consider you or your feelings or your family situation. I really did expect you to drop your life, right where it was, and live mine." His hands slid to her shoulders and tipped her back slightly, to look into her face.

"If you think you feel humiliated, it's nothing compared to how I feel," he said. "Not because you refused to have me," he added hastily, "but because of how I must look in your eyes: a truly arrogant bastard! Now that I can see the whole thing rationally, I can't believe it myself!" He shook his head in self-disgust.

"And my negative attitude about women in the law profession. I'm not sure how that absurd notion became so deeply rooted in my consciousness. It probably goes back to my childhood. All the women I ever knew were dependent on men. No matter how spunky they'd been as girls, in time they had to meekly submit to the men they married. They even sided with their husbands against their own children. There was never any thought of bettering themselves, and they actually opposed having their sons seek a better life than their husbands had had. Melissa, you can't imagine how oppressive it is to be scorned for wanting a life outside the mines." His eyes clouded at the memory.

"Even Grace, the woman I came to admire most, assumed a traditional feminine role. Julia's always been her own boss, but for a long time I thought she was just a fluke. Then I met you, and it started me thinking. The two of you couldn't be that unique in your abilities and ambitions. After looking around I saw there were a number of bright, capable young women perfectly able to handle themselves in the courtroom. I've given orders for my firm to actively recruit them now.

"Lord, I've been such a fool for so long and in so many ways. Do you think you could ever love me?"

As she looked at him, Melissa realized that the torment of suffering had been as great for him as it had been for her. Her heart went out to him. She had never thought to see him so vulnerable as he was at this moment, exposing his very soul to her.

He continued before she could answer. "I had this suite reserved long before you called me. I arranged my business so that I would have a month—or more if I needed it—to ask your forgiveness and to convince you to marry me. My career and ego will never come first again, I promise you that. Your hopes, dreams, and needs will be as dear to me as mine . . . far more dear." He spoke with a depth of sincerity she'd never heard pass his lips.

"You can have your independence, your career, your family . . . I swear to you. But my darling Melissa, I can't live another moment without you. Do you have room in your life for me? Could we build a new life together?"

To look at him it was hard to believe he was the same man she had known. As deeply in love as she had been before, Melissa felt her love take on a new dimension, encompassing, she knew instinctively, all there was for love to hold. Brandon had never been more handsome, more real, more appealing. Seeing the love in his eyes, she knew they held the promise to make her most dearly cherished wishes come true.

He felt the tension leave her body as she accepted his words, reaching up to pull his lips to hers for a lingering kiss that left no doubt as to her feelings.

"I have one more thing to ask you," he whispered against her hair. "And it's so damn ironic, I can hardly believe it myself. Has a woman ever opened a man's eyes as clearly as you?"

"I don't think I understand. In what way?" she questioned.

"It's family, Melissa. I was so dead set against the idea of dependency on family love and loyalty. Then you came along and made me see the truth. I do have a family—I've had one all along. The Raymonds are my family just as certainly as the Bennetts are yours. I've taken their love and support for years without even admitting to myself the important role they played in my life. But this past Christmas changed all that." His voice was a cross between a laugh and a groan. "I found that though I could take all the abuse a courtroom fight or the media had to offer I couldn't bear the combined disapproval of Grace and Julia." He shook his head in wonder. "The judge was even a little distant. They all knew what a damned fool I was to risk losing you.

"Honey, it's become enormously important to me to have my own family." He hesitated. "You, Jana, and . . ."

"And what?" Melissa prompted softly.

"Do you think you could take a little time from your career to have another child . . . my child?" His voice caught with sentiment at what he was asking.

"Oh, Brandon. Yes, yes." Her heart sang with the pure laughter of living. "How could you even ask? It's what I've longed for . . . needed," she answered, smiling tenderly, breathing in the very essence of his masculine aroma.

Lowering his face to the soft skin of her scented neck, he

murmured softly, "I love you so much. Then you'll have me, Melissa?"

Soft breath caressed his ear. "Yes, my darling Brandon. I was destined to love you forever."

Holding her radiant face between strong gentle hands, he gazed at her as if to check memory against reality. Their eyes met in a look of timeless love. Slowly his mouth met hers, then quickened probingly—infinitely tender, yet demandingly drawing from her the answer his aroused body sought . . . the answer her throbbing body yearned to give.

Their lips still sweetly touching in the long embrace, his hands slowly, almost reverently, slid down her slender neck, pushing the soft black velvet from her delicate shoulders, exposing her firm pink-tipped breasts. His eyes hungrily devoured her beauty as she gently extricated her arms from the inhibiting fabric and raised them in love to his strong familiar neck. His hands continued down the satin smooth skin of her back, releasing her compliant body from the constraints of the gown. The exquisite touch of his powerful hands against her flesh as they slid lower, then lower, caused her to tremble with the urgency of desire. His arms encircled her tightly as the pressure on her mouth became more demanding.

The feeling that spread explosively through her body, this feeling she had been afraid would never be hers again, was so marvelous that she gave herself up to the total enjoyment of her senses. His breathing quickened as his hand caressed her softly yielding flesh. She moaned as he buried his dark head between her breasts. Her breathing matched his as she felt the hard masculinity of his closely held body.

There were no words to express the joy of their reunion in love: so great had been their initial attraction for one another, so sweet and brief had been their lovemaking, so painfully excruciating had been the agony of their separation, that they relied only upon their bodies to wordlessly communicate these meanings and truths to each other.

It was altogether natural that Brandon carried Melissa's vibrant pulsing body, her hands joyously untying the perfect bow of the black tie that encircled his neck, into the darkened bedroom for a rapturous celebration of their true and enduring love.

Down in the kitchen of the fine hotel, the staff waited far into the night for suite 920 to call for the elaborate dinner for two that had been so painstakingly and didactically ordered by the handsome, magnetic gentleman earlier in the evening.